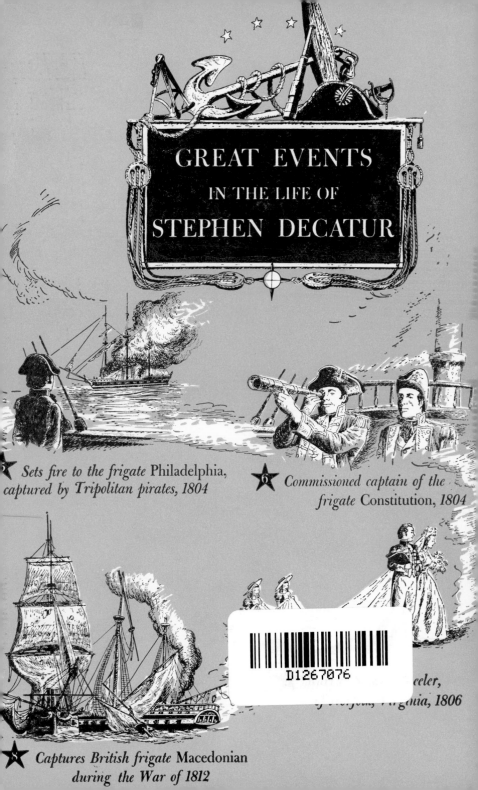

GREAT EVENTS
IN THE LIFE OF
STEPHEN DECATUR

Sets fire to the frigate Philadelphia, *captured by Tripolitan pirates, 1804*

6 *Commissioned captain of the frigate* Constitution, *1804*

...eeler, ...y Norfolk, Virginia, 1806

Captures British frigate Macedonian *during the War of 1812*

THE STORY OF
Stephen Decatur

*He stood at the wheel with his father
and steered the* Ariel

THE STORY OF
Stephen Decatur

By IRIS VINTON

Illustrated by GRAHAM KAYE

ENID LAMONTE MEADOWCROFT
Supervising Editor

PUBLISHERS Grosset & Dunlap NEW YORK

For L. D. G.

Library of Congress Catalog Card No. 54–5861

Contents

[*v*]

Illustrations

THE STORY OF
Stephen Decatur

He could see the ships along the water front

CHAPTER ONE

Rope Climb

SHIPS of all sizes and nations lay along the Front Street water front in Philadelphia. Ships with square sails and ships with three-cornered sails that brought spices and silks, tobacco and cotton, sugar and coffee to be sold at the city market.

All along the water front was the sound of sailors singing. They hauled and stowed cargo and sang lustily, "Hey! ho! away we go, riding on a donkey."

The voices of merchants and captains were heard rising and falling as they bargained about goods. And over everything the smells of roasting coffee, fish, and tar hovered like a fog in the warm June air.

Young Stephen Decatur loved these sights

[*3*]

and sounds and smells. Down on the docks with his father among seafaring men, he forgot that he had ever been sick. He forgot Dr. Rush's medicines. His head did not ache. He was not tired. He felt fine. But just the same, he had to stop to cough every once in a while.

"We had better go home, Stephen," his father said at last.

"Why, I got over the whooping cough long

ago," Stephen told him. "Dr. Rush says all I need now is plenty of fresh air and sunshine." His great black eyes were pleading.

But Captain Decatur had begun to walk so fast that Stephen had to jog-trot to keep up with him. They were hurrying home without even going on board his father's ship. And they could have gone aboard as easily as not. For the *Ariel* was moored right in front of the

office building of Gurney and Smith, the merchants Captain Decatur worked for.

All the way down Front Street, men nodded to the captain. Sailors touched their round straw hats in respect as he passed.

"That's the man who captured the British sloop *Active*," they said.

Stephen often heard people tell how bravely his father had fought in the Revolutionary War which had ended in 1781, just six years before. In that war the Americans had won their freedom from England and had become an independent nation. It made Stephen very proud to know his father had helped by fighting on the sea and capturing a British ship.

As soon as they were home inside their neat brick house, his father told him, "Go outside and play. I want to talk with your mother and grandmother." He smiled and added, "Don't worry, lad."

Stephen put his three-cornered hat beside his father's three-cornered hat on the hall table. He examined his tongue in the mirror above the table. It was pink and clean. He opened his eyes wide. They were clear and sparkling. He did not feel sick. And he

[6]

wouldn't look sick, he thought, if it weren't for his pale, bony face. He blew out his cheeks and roughed up his curly black hair. There! He looked as strong as his friend, Dick Somers, who was as strong as an ox.

He strode outside.

His younger brothers—James, aged six, and John, aged three—were under the chestnut tree at the end of the path. James was chinning himself on a low branch. Little John stood watching him in admiration.

Although James was almost three years younger than Stephen, he was able to do almost everything his brother did. But James had never had to spend weeks in bed with a fever or a cold or a sore throat. James never had anything the matter with him. Stephen always had something wrong. He had grown used to hearing his mother and grandmother say he was "frail." He had heard it so often that he didn't really mind it.

But each time his tall sea-captain father returned from a voyage to France, Stephen wished he could change overnight into what his father called "a stout, brave lad," like the young sailors on the *Ariel*.

[7]

In fact, he wanted to do something right now—something hard to do. The rope climb! He looked up at the new rope which hung from a high branch of the chestnut tree. His father had put it up yesterday.

"Every boy should learn to climb a rope," Captain Decatur had pointed out to Stephen and James. "Especially sons of a seagoing man." And he had shown them how to hoist themselves up and lower themselves down. The boys took turns for a while. James, however, could never remember not to slide down with his hands. After burning his palms several times, he gave up. But Stephen had practiced until Grandmother called them all to supper.

"You shouldn't let Stephen tire himself out," she scolded Stephen's father. "He won't sleep tonight." But Stephen had slept soundly, waking only once with a coughing spell.

Now, running under the chestnut tree, Stephen called out, "Watch me do the rope climb!"

Holding one hand above his head, the other at chest level, he grasped the rope. Then with one leg behind the rope and the right leg in

[*8*]

front, he started up. A second later, he had
fallen hard on his knees. He sat down to in-
spect them. He had torn holes in his black
stockings. And his bare bony knees were
scratched and bruised.

He heard the rattle of dishes as his sister
came into the garden with the tea tray. It was
heaped with cinnamon toast, butter and jam,
hot milk, and a pot of weak tea. She set the
tray down on the white iron table and rushed
over to Stephen.

"Did you hurt yourself?" Priscilla asked.

Stephen shook his head. His sister and his
brothers were staring at him as though something terrible had happened.

It made him angry. He was not such a baby
that a little thing like falling down would
make him cry.

"You had better not be hurt," Priscilla
went on, tossing back her long braids. "Papa
is very worried about you. I just heard him tell
Mama and Grandmother that you weren't
well and something had to be done about it.
You're nothing but skin and bones."

"Just skin and bones," repeated his brother
James.

"Bones," echoed his brother John.

"I'd rather be skinny than a great big ox like you," Stephen declared. He glared fiercely at his sister.

"Stephen Decatur!" exclaimed Priscilla. "Don't you dare call me an ox!"

"Well, you are," stated Stephen, for no reason at all. Getting up from the ground, he took hold of the rope again. "I wish you would all go away."

He began to climb, remembering this time to clinch the rope with his knees and to hold fast with his legs and feet.

"Don't you want anything to eat?" asked Priscilla.

From six feet off the ground, he glanced down at them. "No, thank you," he replied politely. "I've lost my appetite."

He truthfully was not hungry now. He felt all stirred up inside. Sometimes the least thing —like calling him skin and bones—made him feel that way. And all he wanted was to be left alone.

He raised his head. The branch of the tree seemed a long way up. He would not think how far it was. He would just climb. Placing one hand over the other, he lifted himself with his arms. He raised his knees and clinched the rope. Gripping with legs and feet, he straightened his hips. The branch was a little nearer. He reached up with his other hand. Lift, clinch, straighten; reach, lift, clinch, straighten—up he went. He climbed higher and higher until he could see over the garden wall.

He could see the Delaware River and the ships along the water front. He could even pick out the *Ariel* among the brigs and barques, schooners and frigates. His thin arms and legs ached. But he kept climbing. Before long, leaves brushed his face. The branch where the rope was tied was right above his head. His nose felt raw from breathing hard. His shoulders and back seemed numb. He put up one hand, then the other quickly and held on. Pushing against the rope with his feet, he swung himself onto the limb. He'd made it!

He sat astride, panting from his exercise, but feeling very pleased with himself. From his perch, he had a fine view of the city. Over there on Chestnut Street was the State House. "That's where the Declaration of Independence was signed on July 4, 1776, three years before you were born," his father had told him. "The American Colonies declared their freedom from England. And your grandmother and I stood in the yard outside the State House and heard the Declaration read to the crowd."

Over on Third and Pine Streets was St. Peter's Episcopal Church where the family went every Sunday. Someday, if he became a minister, as his mother and grandmother wanted him to, he would preach there. He would get up in the pulpit and—

His sister's voice broke in sharply on his daydreaming. "Stephen Decatur, come down from there!" she ordered curtly. "You're going to fall."

"I am not," denied Stephen, clicking the heels of his silver-buckle shoes together. His brothers' upturned faces were full of grins. They loved a show of daring. But twelve-year-old Priscilla was stamping her foot. "Come down this instant!" she demanded loudly.

That gave him an idea. "This very minute?" he asked. Without waiting for her to answer, he pulled the rope up part way and clung to it tightly. Crying, "Watch out below!" he jumped.

Priscilla screamed.

The weight of Stephen's body jerked the rope taut. Out he sailed, his head thrown back and his legs dangling. The three hopped around, shouting warnings. For a moment Stephen swung helplessly back and forth in the air. The rope slipped away each time he tried to clutch it between his feet. What was it his father had told him yesterday?

Like a flash he remembered how to get down, using only his hands. He swung his body left, brought down his right hand, grabbed the rope. Then he wriggled his body to the right, brought his left hand down, gripped the rope. Right hand, left hand, right hand, left hand, swaying his body from one side to the other at the same time—he quickly lowered himself.

His toes touched earth. He was dizzy. He trembled from head to foot. But he had done it! He let go the rope and toppled over on the grass.

Water splashed in his face. Opening his eyes, he saw Priscilla bending over him with

[*13*]

an empty glass. James and John were sitting on their heels staring at him curiously.

"You fainted," gasped his sister.

"I did not," Stephen contradicted, propping himself up on his elbows. Then he saw his father and Dr. Rush coming toward him down the garden path. Behind them were his mother and grandmother. His heart sank. They were going to put him to bed again after all. He couldn't bear it!

CHAPTER TWO

A Taste of Salt

HIS mother and grandmother darted in front of the two men. "Oh, Stephen, what happened?" his mother cried.

She bent down and felt of his forehead. It was cool. She sighed with relief. At least, he wasn't feverish.

Stephen got up and began to brush the dirt off his good clothes, although his hands still trembled.

"You can see, Ann, he isn't hurt," Decatur said to his wife.

"You shouldn't take such violent exercise until you're stronger, Stephen," his mother warned.

"You gave us quite a turn," his grand-

[*15*]

mother said. She smoothed his hair back and straightened his tie.

"I'm fine, Grandmother." Stephen spoke rather crossly. He wished they wouldn't make such a fuss over him.

Captain Decatur put one hand under his wife's elbow and the other under his mother's. "Come," he said brightly, gently urging them away. "Take Priscilla and the boys and go inside. The doctor and I want to talk with Stephen."

When they had gone, Captain Decatur said, "You know, Stephen, no matter what you want to be when you grow up, you'll need to be strong and healthy."

"I know," Stephen agreed. "But I'm already lots better."

"But that isn't good enough," said Dr. Rush. "We want you to be well. And I think the best thing for you right now is a sea voyage."

Captain Decatur broke in quickly. "Next Wednesday when I sail for Bordeaux, Stephen, I'll take you with me. Now, what do you say to that?"

"Go with you to France!" exclaimed Stephen. "I'd like that better than anything."

So it was decided that Stephen should go to France. At once his mother and grandmother began getting him ready for the voyage. He would be gone for months. A week was none too long a time for all that had to be done.

On Monday two trunks were carried down from the attic. On Tuesday they were packed. On Wednesday morning a man came and took them in his cart to the ship.

Stephen never could remember afterwards how the family got to the wharf. For the next thing he remembered was being on the *Ariel*, looking down at everyone. And they were calling "good-by's" and "don't forget's" to him.

At the same time, he could hear his father giving orders. The ship moved out from the wharf. She was towed into the middle of the river by men in two boats. Then his father dismissed the boats and gave the command to get the ship under way.

At once the whole ship leaped into life. Men grasped lines and hauled. There were shrill calls of the boatswain and his mates. At Captain Decatur's direction the first mate bawled orders through a trumpet. Men climbed to the yards. Square sails as big as clouds opened up. They caught the breeze and the *Ariel* floated down the Delaware.

The people on the wharf were only a blur now. Everything gradually melted into the blue sky. It came to Stephen suddenly that he

was going away from home. He wouldn't be back for a long time.

His throat tightened. He started to cough. Putting his arm over his face, he began to run toward his father's cabin at the stern of the ship. He bumped into someone.

"Lad, this is not the time for playing blind man's buff," a sailor's voice warned.

A big hand took hold of his sleeve and steered him in the other direction. "Sit you

down on the hatch cover," the man said. "After you've coughed your heels up, you'll be right as rain. You got that cough ashore. The climate is very, very unhealthy on land."

[19]

Stephen, in spite of coughing, had to laugh.

"Seafaring is the only life for a man," declared the sailor. He gave Stephen a friendly clap on the arm and went on about his work.

Stephen continued to sit on the hatch, after his coughing spell was over. He watched and listened. Putting to sea was exciting.

The water in the Delaware was unusually low. The captain had to be careful not to run the ship aground. So he sent two lookouts to the little platforms at the top of the masts. They called out the landmarks—the points of land, islands, sand bars, rocks—to help guide the ship.

Above the noise of the sailors on deck rose piercing cries of "By the mark five. By the mark five."

Leaving the hatch cover, Stephen ran in the direction of the cries. On climbing to the top of the bulwark, he saw the leadsmen taking soundings to find the depth of the water. One of them whirled a line with a lead weight on it and cast it as far as he could. When the lead struck bottom, the men hauled it up. They looked at the markings on the line and called out how deep the water was.

Their "by the mark five" and then "by the mark seven" rang throughout the ship to let the captain and the helmsman know the water was thirty to forty-two feet deep. That was more than deep enough for the *Ariel*.

By nightfall the land was left far behind and the open sea was before them. Stephen had explored the ship from end to end. At last he went back to the stern near his father's cabin. He watched a porpoise leaping and diving for a while.

Soon the odors of supper cooking drifted back from the galley halfway down the deck. His mouth watered. He was suddenly so hungry, he could hardly wait. A steward came out of the galley and headed his way. Stephen darted into the cabin.

His father was studying a chart of the *Ariel's* course—a sort of sea road map. He pushed it aside as Stephen entered.

"Supper's coming," Stephen announced. "I could eat a horse."

"Now, that's very lucky," his father remarked, grinning broadly. "Because we're going to have salt horse."

Stephen ate salt horse that night and many

[*21*]

times afterwards. He liked the taste of the salt beef with boiled potatoes and onions. Perhaps it was just that he was hungry all the time. His father often joked about how his son was eating him out of ship and cargo.

Before long, Stephen's clothes did not fit. And Sails, the seaman who mended and repaired the canvas ship's sails, had to lengthen jacket sleeves and let out seams.

"You're growing, that's what you are," Sails told the boy. He felt of Stephen's arms. "And you've quite a muscle there."

"Oh, yes, I'm getting to be very strong," Stephen boasted.

These days he often surprised himself. He ran about the ship from morning until night without feeling tired. He climbed the rungs of the ratlines with the sailors. They showed him how to hang by his knees from the ropes. He helped haul on lines. On calm days, he often stood at the wheel with his father and steered the *Ariel*.

Sometimes at night he woke up. And he lay there in his bunk, thinking about his mother or James, perhaps. He liked thinking about them with the men on watch walking the deck. And the ship's bells sounding the half-hours quick and clear. He could smell the salt spray and lick the salt off his chapped lips. It had a good taste!

Then one morning there was a rush of feet across the deck. He could hear sailors stumbling up from the forecastle. He got into his clothes and dashed out of the cabin. Captain Decatur was already on deck commanding the crew.

"Shorten sail!" he cried.

Sails were clewed up. The ship, which had

been bounding swiftly across the ocean, slowed down and swung into the muddy waters of the Gironde River. She glided between the green banks. Stephen leaned over the rail, gazing at the fields and cattle and farmhouses of the French countryside. He thought it looked very much like the Delaware valley at home.

Captain Decatur strolled over and stood beside the sturdy figure of his son. The sun-browned, eager face scarcely seemed to belong to the frail boy that he had brought aboard weeks ago.

[*24*]

Very soon the city of Bordeaux appeared on their right. The *Ariel* crept toward the wharves and tied up in front of the big main square. Some boys fishing from the dock stopped to stare at the American ship with the Stars and Stripes floating from the mast. Seeing Stephen, they waved and called out greetings.

Stephen flourished his hat at them. It really wasn't so very different from home, he thought.

CHAPTER THREE

Dr. Abercrombie's Four

M AMA, somebody took my ice skates!"
Stephen cried. It was past noon of a winter's
day and he was in the storeroom off the
kitchen, hunting for his skates. In this catch-
all were fish poles and shinny sticks, balls and
beanbags, an axe for chopping wood, and a
bucket for carrying water from the well.

"I wish people would leave my things
alone," Stephen muttered. By "people" he
meant his brothers, James and John.

His mother came to the storeroom door. She
watched him shoving chests and boxes about
to look behind them. It made her happy to see
him so healthy and strong. Ever since he had
come home from France, he had not been sick
once. He was now a sturdy eleven-year-old.

"You'll be late for school this afternoon," she warned. "Why don't you wait to look for your skates until you have more time?"

"Because we want to go skating right after school," Stephen replied. "You said I could, Mother." He glanced around, then straightened up. "Well, I just can't find them, that's all." He sighed.

"Find what?" asked John, wobbling in on a pair of ice skates.

"My skates!" yelled Stephen. "You take off my skates this minute, John Decatur."

John calmly undid the straps and handed the skates to his brother.

"I wasn't hurting them any," he remarked.

"Maybe not," Stephen said, "but next time, ask me first if you can have them." He buttoned up his greatcoat, slung the skates over his shoulder, and called, "James! I'm ready."

Mrs. Decatur covered her ears. "Not so loud, please. James is waiting outside for you," she told him.

Stephen kissed his mother. He said good-by to John and went bounding out the door, shouting good-by's to his grandmother and Priscilla, who were upstairs.

James quit throwing snowballs at the lamp-post in front of the house. He fell into step beside Stephen, and the two hurried toward the Episcopal Academy a few blocks away on Fourth Street. The air was dry and still and the snow crunched beneath their heavy boots. It was wonderful skating weather.

Waiting on the corner, swinging their skates, were Stephen's best friends—Richard Rush, Charles Stewart, and Dick Somers. They joined Stephen, and the four continued up the steet with James tagging behind.

They were still a block away when the school bell began to clang. Dr. Abercrombie, the headmaster of the academy, was on the steps, with a bell in one hand and a rattan cane in the other. A line of boys was already forming before the steps. Those who were tardy in entering the doors could expect a lick on the legs from the cane.

The five boys raced pell-mell up the street. They got in line not a moment too soon, for the headmaster's hand was on the knob, ready to close the door. They marched into the building as stiffly as wooden soldiers, hung up their coats, and went to their seats.

*Those who were tardy could expect a lick
on the legs from the cane*

Dr. Abercrombie took his place at the front of the room. He was a gloomy figure in his black coat and breeches and hose. Although the boys were not making a sound, he shouted, "Silence! Now get to work, every one of you."

Gloom soon settled over the classroom as the pupils set grimly about their lessons for the afternoon. The headmaster believed that the more unhappy the boys appeared, the more they must be learning.

But it was dull to have to write, "Good words cost nothing but are worth much," until every letter was perfect. And grammar was even duller with one rule after the other to memorize. Yet Stephen studied hard. Each time his thoughts strayed to ice skating, he pulled them back to his books. He felt that the afternoon would never end.

Dr. Abercrombie was looking at the clock. It was time for arithmetic class. The last thing every afternoon, Stephen had to pick his way through arithmetic problems as though they were a brier patch. Every new problem was full of thorns to snag him. But today, as good luck would have it, was review day.

"I trust you boys are prepared," the headmaster said, taking a sheet of paper from his desk.

Stephen's face lit up. He had studied hard the night before, going over past problems with his mother. He smiled at Richard and Dick and Charles. They returned his smile with glum looks. Stephen might be happy about a review, but they weren't.

"A farmer has five and one-half acres of ground to plant in potatoes," Dr. Abercrombie read from the paper. "If it takes sixteen bushels of seed potatoes to plant two acres, how many bushels will the farmer need for five and a half acres?"

"There he goes with his potatoes again," thought Stephen. Why there were never any problems about interesting things like ships or sailing was a mystery to him. But he worked out the answer quickly—forty-four bushels. He sat up and folded his hands on his desk. He was the first to finish.

The headmaster gave out the second problem. And a third. Then a fourth. And the same thing happened. Stephen was first to finish each time.

Dr. Abercrombie had been walking up and

down the aisles, peering over the boys' shoulders as they worked. Now he stopped beside Stephen to examine his paper.

"So far, Decatur, you are the only boy properly prepared for his review," observed the headmaster. "You've already shown you know your lesson, so we won't waste your time. You are dismissed for the day."

"Thank you, sir," Stephen sang out. Think of all the extra time he'd have to skate! He put on his coat, snatched up his ice skates, and dashed out of the building.

It never occurred to him until he was outside that there was no one to go skating with him.

James, who was dismissed at two-thirty with the little boys, found him moping on the steps. A few minutes later, James and his friends were on their way home, throwing snowballs at each other. Stephen was left, stamping from one foot to the other and slapping his arms about himself to keep warm. He wasn't so sure that he liked this sort of reward for knowing his lesson.

It was after three o'clock when his class was dismissed. Dick and Charles and Richard surrounded him. They seemed very serious. And Dick said crossly, "Come on, let's get on to the river, if we're going."

They ran the whole way to the Schuylkill River, which flowed through the city of Philadelphia. There were already a number of young men and women skating. They were gliding slowly about in a great circle over the clear, hard ice. Stephen and his friends, however, were the first boys to arrive from school.

[33]

As they sat down on the snowy bank to put on their skates, Stephen asked, "What's the matter? I waited for you, didn't I? And none of you hardly spoke to me on the way over."

"Shall we tell him?" Charles looked at Dick and Richard.

"Go ahead, if you want to," Dick said. "I—"

He never finished his sentence. For the other boys in the class, led by Tom McCall, came bursting through the dry marsh reeds like cannon balls.

Tom halted in front of Dick Somers. "Coward!" he spat out. "You ran off. You're afraid to fight."

Dick got up slowly with his hands on his hips. He towered over the short McCall boy.

"Afraid, am I?" Dick said. "You're not big enough to scare a flea. When I fight, I fight somebody my own size. I told you that before. Now go away."

Tom did not bother to reply. He lashed out at Dick's face. Dick grabbed the other's arm and twisted it. Tom howled.

"Still want to fight?" asked Dick.

"Yes," Tom grunted.

"Then bring on your brother Bill," Dick

ordered, letting go the boy's arm. "To make it fair, I'll fight you both at the same time."

Tom's brother darted from the group of boys and came at Dick Somers, fists flying. And the two McCalls hurled themselves at him furiously. Dick defended himself with well-aimed punches at first one McCall and then the other. Soon the two began to dance around him and Dick began swinging wild. One of his wild swings missed a McCall and hit an on-looker on the chin.

All the other boys had been watching the fight, shouting noisily, but not interfering. Now the onlooker who had been hit waded in. He punched Dick in the back.

That was enough for Stephen.

"Unfair! Unfair!" he cried, punching the onlooker. There were now three against two —Stephen and Dick against the other three boys.

Soon all five were down, rolling over and over on the ice. Though no one was really being badly hurt, it looked like a terrible fight. It went on for such a long time that the audi-ence began to lose interest. Several of the boys put on their skates and skimmed off across the ice. Finally, the only ones left watching were Charles Stewart and Richard Rush.

"Why don't you call quits?" Charles suggested to the McCalls.

"We will, if they will," the McCall brothers said.

"We'll quit if you don't call us quitters," Stephen panted.

Dick agreed and they all stumbled wearily to their feet. They brushed snow and mud from their rumpled and torn clothes. Then all seven boys crouched down and solemnly strapped on their skates.

"What were you fighting McCall for?" Stephen asked Dick, merely as a matter of curiosity.

"He said you cheated in arithmetic," replied Dick mildly. "That's an insult. I told him to take it back. He said come on and fight. And I said when he found somebody big enough, I would."

"I didn't exactly say Stephen cheated," denied the older McCall brother. "I just thought it was very peculiar he got through first today, that's all. Usually he's poor in arithmetic."

"Well, I didn't cheat," said Stephen. He

[*36*]

stood up and balanced himself on his skates.

"I believe you," McCall told him. "Race you to High Street bridge."

With whoops, the seven boys tore off. The fight was forgotten. They were all friends again.

CHAPTER FOUR

The Blue Cockade

Up THE Delaware River from Philadelphia was Windmill Island. It was a wild, wooded spot where no one lived. During the summer, Stephen and his three best friends went there often to swim, fish, and explore. Sometimes a fourth friend, named Hamilton, went too. They always took along an extra boy. Usually this extra boy was a younger brother. The older boys paid him to look after their clothes, while they swam around the island.

They would start soon after dinner at noon. Striking out along the river, they would walk until they were opposite the northern end of Windmill Island. There they would shed hats, shirts, breeches, shoes, and hose. These they would give to the "hired" boy.

Then, diving into the river, they would swim to the island. After wading, fishing, and swimming along the shore, they would reach the south end of the island. By that time, it was usually late afternoon. And they would swim out into the river and let the tide carry them back to the Philadelphia shore. There, in a grove of trees near Joshua Humphreys' ship-yard, they would find the "hired" boy waiting with their clothes.

One afternoon in mid-July when Stephen was about fourteen, he and his friends made one of their excursions to Windmill Island. He, Richard, Charles, Dick, and young Ham-ilton lay stretched out on the grass in the shade. It was growing late. But they felt so lazy and comfortable, they didn't want to get up and go home.

After a while, Stephen thought he heard a shot down the river. He raised his head and listened. He heard another. The other boys sat up and looked at each other.

"Somebody's shooting off a musket," Ste-phen said.

"Sounds like it," Charles agreed. "Let's go see."

Hopping up, they ran to the beach and peered downstream. Below the island was a boat crowded with sailors. Oars flashed in the sun, as the rowers pulled for the Philadelphia shore. A tricolored flag waved from a pole at the stern.

While the boys watched, a sailor fired his gun into the air. A puff of gray-white smoke spurted over the water. And, roaring a cheer, the sailors began to sing at the top of their voices.

"I know! I know now!" Stephen exclaimed. "They're French sailors off one of the French ships anchored in the river."

"That's it!" cried young Hamilton. "They're celebrating. The French have got rid of their bad king. They had a revolutionary war just the way we did. Now France is a republic just like we are here in the United States."

"The French Revolution ended last January," Stephen reminded him. "And now France is at war with England and Holland and Spain. The French minister is here in the

United States—right here in Philadelphia—
to see if we will help France."

"Well, I think we ought to help them," declared Charles. "When we were fighting to get
free from England, France helped us."

Stephen looked very wise. "My father says
that we should stay out of the wars in Europe,"
he told the others. "We ought to be neutral."

"Maybe your father ought to tell that to the
French minister," suggested Dick, grinning.

"Maybe he will," Stephen replied good-
naturedly. "My father and mother are going to
the reception tonight for the minister." Dart-
ing away, he ran splashing into the water.
"Last one across the river is a polecat," he
called.

The others plunged into the stream. They
swam with little effort, being swept along by
the current toward shore. A short time later,
they stood dripping in the grove of elm and
mulberry trees near Mr. Humphreys' ship-
yard.

James came running up with their clothes
in a haversack, which he dragged behind him.

"You just missed seeing a sight!" he announced.

[41]

"What kind of a sight?" Stephen asked. He took the haversack from James and dumped the clothes on the grass.

"Some French sailors came ashore from a boat a little while ago," James said. "They yelled, 'Liberty!' and began dancing around and singing *Le Marseillaise*. And then they threw their liberty caps, with blue, white and red ribbons on them, up in the air. They acted crazy as loons."

"Oh, they're just feeling gay," Stephen said. He tucked his shirt into his knee breeches. He

picked out his three-cornered hat from the pile on the ground. "Looks like you sat on my hat," he accused James. He knocked it into shape and pressed out the ribbons of the blue rosette between his thumb and fingers. "You just about mashed my blue cockade," he scolded. "If you aren't more careful I won't pay you my five cents."

In a few minutes, they were on their way back to town. Because of the heat, some wore no jackets. But their damp heads were jauntily crowned with three-cornered hats, each deco-

rated with an American cockade of blue.

It was only a short distance to the Front Street wharves. They could hear men singing *Le Marseillaise,* the French revolutionary song. Then singing the American song, *Yankee Doodle.*

"Those French sailors started everybody singing, I bet," James remarked. And he began to sing himself. Stephen and the others took up the tune and went whistling along the street. Soon, one after the other, the boys turned off at the different corners to go home.

"Good-by, see you tomorrow," each boy called as he left.

Finally there were only Stephen and James and young Hamilton. Since they lived on Front Street, they continued along the wharves. They kept hearing songs and cheers.

"Hooray for the citizens of France!" a man began to shout. "Hooray for the Tricolor, the flag of liberty!"

The noise was coming from a crowd milling about in front of the Buck's Head Tavern. The boys stopped to see what was going on. People were gathered around a group of French sailors who were doing a sailor's dance.

And everyone—Americans and French alike
—were cheering for liberty and France.

"Down with England!" they were shouting.
"Down with Holland! Down with Spain!"

"See, some Americans are for joining
France in the war," young Hamilton ob-

served. "Look! The Americans are pinning
blue, white, and red ribbons on their hats."

"Come on," Stephen said. "We don't want
to be mixed up in it. Let's go down to the
Ariel. Father's crew is loading tobacco. We
can watch them for a while."

The three boys swung out to pass the crowd.

"Take off that blue cockade," ordered a
rough voice.

[45]

Directly in front of Stephen swayed one of the town bullies. Amid cheers of approval, he thrust a blue, red, and white cockade at the boy.

"Wear this in your hat," he shouted. "Show which side you're on."

"That's young Decatur," a man called out. "His father has made plenty of money trading with France. He ought to sport the French colors in his hat."

"I'll do no such thing," Stephen cried. "I don't ask the French to wear American cockades. The French should wear their own colors. But I'm an American. I'm going to wear my blue cockade."

"We'll see about that!" exclaimed the bully. He reached out to grab Stephen's hat. Stephen pushed the arm away.

The bully pushed Stephen, making him stumble backward. Recovering his balance, Stephen rushed at the bully. It did not matter that the other was twice his size.

A fight started quickly. Several other rowdies leaped in to help the bully, and James and young Hamilton added their blows to Stephen's. The three boys were no match for the burly rowdies, but the men in the crowd urged them on.

"Lick 'em, Decatur! You landed one then, Decatur! Let 'em have it, boys!" they yelled.

Finally a man shouted, "Guards! Where are the guards! Somebody stop the fight before them boys is killed!"

The brawl could be heard the length of the water front. The name of Decatur reached the ears of the *Ariel's* crew. A dozen or more sailors dropped their work. They raced up the street and elbowed their way through the crowd. Seeing the Decatur boys getting a frightful beating, the sailors flayed about with arms and fists. Very soon, they had dragged the

[47]

bruised and bleeding boys away from the rowdies.

Stephen could scarcely stand. But he looked around for his hat. It lay trampled on the street. Picking it up, he dusted it off against his leg, and set it carefully on his head.

"I'll still fight the next fellow who tries to take off my blue cockade," he declared, as he limped off.

CHAPTER FIVE

The Raft

IT WAS a June night three years later. Stephen was again on the Delaware River. This time he was floating down the river on a raft of big logs. With him were four men—the pilot, his helper, a roustabout, and one of Mr. Humphreys' shipwrights. The logs were to be used in building a new frigate for the Navy. And the men were taking them to Joshua Humphreys' shipyard downriver.

Stephen sat cross-legged before his sea box. A drawing of the frame of the new frigate was spread out on it. He and the shipwright were studying the plan by the glow of a lantern.

"Mr. Humphreys is going to be very pleased, I can tell you," the shipwright said.

"When he gets these logs by tomorrow morning, his shipyard will be the first to begin work on a new frigate."

"What about the shipyards at Boston, New York, Norfolk, Baltimore, and Portsmouth?" asked Stephen. He smiled up at the gray-haired craftsman. "They're supposed to start building frigates for the Navy too."

"They'll have trouble getting such logs as these," said the man. "All we had to do was go up the Delaware. Cross over into the New Jersey forest. Pick out the best white oak trees, fell them, make a raft and float back to the yard." He paused, then went on. "It didn't take you long to learn to choose the best wood. You've an eye for what makes a fine ship. You might say, you're a born seafaring man, Stephen."

Stephen gave a mock groan. "Don't ever say that, sir, when my mother can hear you," he cautioned.

"She'd rather you didn't think about ships at all, I suppose," remarked the shipwright drily.

Stephen nodded. "But she finally agreed with Father and me that I wouldn't make a good minister," he said. "That's why Father got me this job as clerk with Gurney & Smith. I was wasting my time at the University of Pennsylvania."

"Oh, now, I wouldn't say that," the shipwright drawled with a twinkle in his eyes. "You learned something there. That's a fine drawing, showing how the *United States* is going to look when she's finished. But I must say, I never before knew a clerk who spent all his free time studying mathematics and making pictures of ships."

"I'm not really interested in being a clerk," Stephen admitted rather sheepishly. "And I'm afraid I never will be."

Stephen rolled up his drawing. Lifting the lid of his sea box, he put it away with his other things. Then he and the shipwright walked to the stern where the pilot was guiding the raft with a long steering oar.

The sky was clouding over, shutting out the stars. Soon the wind began to moan and the thunder to grumble.

"Looks like it might be making up for a summer storm," the pilot ventured.

It wasn't long before the storm struck.

There was a flash of lightning that streaked across the sky. It was followed by a tremendous clap of thunder. And the rain poured from the clouds. The wind blew. The raft boomed downriver with the waves frothing off the sides.

"Everybody at the sweeps," called the pilot. "We'll have to keep her in the middle of the river."

Stephen took one of the long oars, called sweeps. He scrambled to his place up front at the side of the raft. Straddling his long legs, he rowed or dragged his sweep as the pilot directed. The shipwright, the pilot's helper, and the roustabout were all using their oars to keep the raft in midstream.

The raft plunged on faster and faster. Spray flew up, hitting Stephen's face hard enough to make him gasp. With the cold rain and spray pelting him, he was wet to the skin and shivering. But he scarcely noticed it. He was too excited.

The lightning quivered overhead suddenly. And the pilot cried, "Look out! Island ahead there! Pull to larboard!"

It was Windmill Island. And they were

bearing straight down on it. The shock of striking the shore would burst the raft apart. They must have been traveling at a great rate, Stephen thought, to reach the island so quickly. He pushed as hard as he could with his oar to help swing the raft to the left. The water whirled about. And the raft pitched as though caught in an eddy.

"Pull, men, pull!" yelled the pilot. "Bring her head into the current."

Stephen remembered the swift current which ran past the east side of Windmill Island. He dipped deep into the water again with his long oar and pulled.

For a moment, the raft trembled, and the water rushing against his legs almost upset him. Then the raft jerked to larboard. Putting all their strength into a final pull on their oars, the men swung her into the current. Everyone gave a shout as the raft went gliding swiftly past the island toward the south end.

"This current will carry us to the shipyard," Stephen called out happily. "When we boys used to come to the island, that's the way we'd swim back home."

The rain let up and the wind died down.

The summer storm was over. As they drifted toward Philadelphia, the stars came out again. They saw a light on the shore.

"That light's in Mr. Humphreys' ship-yard!" Stephen cried. "We're going to get there long before morning."

They shoved for the light. Soon they were maneuvering the raft up to the shipyard dock.

And there was Mr. Humphreys. Captain John Barry of the Navy was with him and so was the yard's watchman. They were all waiting to give a hand with the mooring.

"We were just leaving the yard when we saw you starting across from Windmill Island," explained Mr. Humphreys. "There they come

[55]

with the logs, I told the captain. We can start laying the keel for the ship as soon as it's daylight. You're all to be congratulated for getting here so quickly."

"Well, Stephen," said Captain Barry, as the boy left the raft, "you've had a part in the beginning of a new ship."

"I only wish, sir, I could be on deck when she puts to sea," Stephen told him.

But he knew, even as he spoke, that there was little chance of his sailing on the frigate. It had been a great disappointment to his mother that he had not wanted to become a minister.

"And it has been hard for her to have my father away so much of the time," Stephen thought as he walked home in the starlight. "I shall never tell my mother that I want to go to sea."

CHAPTER SIX

Down to the Sea

ON A May morning two years later, Stephen crouched above his high clerk's desk at Gurney & Smith. He was writing out the latest news of ships. It was mostly bad news. The more he wrote, the angrier he became.

He jabbed his pen into the pewter inkwell and added: "The barque *Patience* was captured by the French off the Bahamas. The sloop *Sally* was sunk by a French cutter."

Stephen muttered, "The French are picking us off like sitting ducks."

"You're right," agreed a ship's captain, stopping on his way to Mr. Gurney's private office. "Girard over on High Street lost another brig. I saw it fired on outside Southampton, England. It sank with all hands. Write it down."

"Yes, sir," Stephen said. "That makes over three hundred American vessels they've captured or sunk."

"Don't care if it's six hundred," said the captain in a stubborn voice. "The French aren't going to chase us off the ocean." He glared at the news sheet.

"That's the way to talk!" cried a young skipper who had just come in from the street. "I was only two gunshots ahead of a French sloop-of-war all the way from the West Indies. Got away by the skin of my teeth. Maybe I can't outfight 'em. But I can outrun 'em."

He followed the captain into Mr. Gurney's office.

Stephen dug his pen fiercely into his paper. It seemed to him that he had to listen every day to reports of the sinking or capture of American ships.

The trouble had all come about because France was at war with England. She was determined that the United States should not trade with England. The United States declared that the seas all over the world were free. Americans intended to trade with any country that wanted to buy and sell goods,

[*58*]

whether France liked it or not. So American ships continued to sail everywhere. And the French continued to capture many of them.

Stephen finished the last item of news. Easing himself off the stool, he went to the win-

dow to post the bulletin. As always, there were people outside, waiting to get the latest report. Their faces became red with anger as soon as they commenced to read. Some of the men shook their fists and swore at the bad news. Their voices came through the half-opened window.

"How much longer are we going to let them

Frenchmen get away with sinking our ships?" one of them demanded.

"Not much longer," replied a weather-beaten sailor. "That new frigate *United States* is going to be ready for sea any day now."

"And when Captain Decatur finishes repairs on that ship, *Delaware*," said another, "why, we'll begin to have a real navy. With Captain Barry on the *United States* and Captain Decatur on the *Delaware*, we're going to start defending ourselves. And don't you forget it!"

"I wish I could forget it," Stephen thought impatiently. "All I want is to get into the Navy, and here I am, pushing a pen all day! I'd better get back to work, too."

He strode to his desk and began making a clean copy of an order for ammunition for the frigates' guns, which Mr. Humphreys had given him. Soon he was interested in his work. The morning passed quickly. It wasn't until the middle of the afternoon that he felt himself growing restless.

"Perhaps Mr. Gurney has a message for someone in the State House," he thought. "I'd do anything to get out of the office."

He was on the point of asking Mr. Gurney if he didn't have an errand for him when Captain Barry entered.

"Good afternoon, Stephen," the captain said jovially. He was a strong, ruddy-faced man with a big nose and pleasant mouth. "Are the heads of the firm here?"

Stephen slid off his stool. "Good afternoon, sir. Mr. Gurney's in his office. I'll tell him—"

"Don't bother," said the captain, brushing past him. "I'll go right in."

For a moment there was a murmur of voices behind Mr. Gurney's closed door. Then Captain Barry came out, looking pleased and a little excited.

"Mr. Gurney says you're to clean off your desk and come along with me," Captain Barry told Stephen.

The idea of getting away from pen, ink, and paper was too delightful to be spoiled by asking questions. As they left the office, Captain Barry started to talk about how he was going to train young men for the Navy. And he kept it up all the way down Front Street. When they reached the Decatur house, the captain turned in.

[*61*]

"But why are we going here?" Stephen asked, speaking for the first time.

"To see your mother, of course," answered Captain Barry.

The maid who let them in said Stephen's mother was alone in the parlor. When Mrs. Decatur saw Captain Barry and her son walk in, she was astonished. "Why, Stephen, you're never home until after six!" she exclaimed. "What brings you back so early?"

"I brought him, ma'am," replied the captain, sitting down in a chair near her. At once, he began talking about how badly young men were needed for the Navy.

"To build a fine, strong United States Navy, ma'am," he said, "we must have young men of fine character and high ideals. We need men who can be trained to become officers."

"I know," Mrs. Decatur said softly. "Now tell me what this has to do with Stephen."

"Just this," answered Captain Barry. He took a rolled sheet of heavy paper from the pocket of his blue uniform and handed it to her.

Unrolling it, she read aloud: "To Stephen Decatur—I hereby appoint you Midshipman

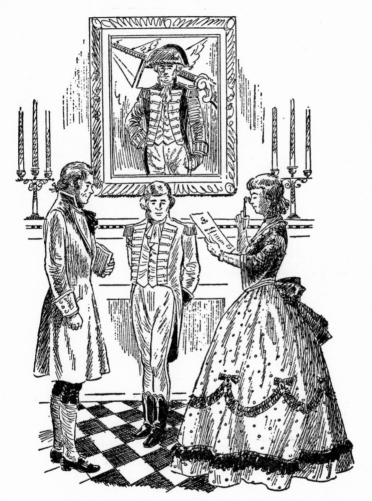

Her eyes drifted to the foot of the page

in the Navy of the United States." Her eyes drifted to the foot of the page. It was signed, "John Adams, President of the United States." And the date was April 30, 1798.

She lowered the paper slowly. Her eyes were troubled as she looked at Stephen. Her son's eyes were bright as stars. His cheeks were flushed with excitement. At the thought of going to sea, he had become a new person.

"He looks better than he has in months," Mrs. Decatur said to herself. "He'll never be happy working in an office. He belongs on a ship and I must not try to keep him at home any longer." Turning to Captain Barry, she asked quietly, "When must he report?"

The captain smiled broadly. "You're a wise woman, ma'am, and a brave one," he said. "It takes courage for a mother to let her son follow the sea."

Then, getting up, he answered her question. "Stephen is to report to me on the *United States* next week, Mrs. Decatur."

CHAPTER SEVEN

Mr. Midshipman Decatur

STEPHEN stood before the tall mirror in the tailor shop, twisting and turning, trying to see how he looked in his new uniform. There were still white basting threads in the blue coat which had round cuffs faced with red, and a stand-up collar. But the blue breeches were finished, and so was the red waistcoat.

"It fits very well," he told the tailor, as the man helped him take it off. "I'll stop by tomorrow and pick it up."

A few moments later he was hurrying home. Racing up the stairs to his room, he began to pack some books and drawing materials.

His mother, who sat sewing in the room below, heard him whistle as he worked.

"He's nineteen," she thought. "And he's just as excited about going to sea as he was when he was nine and going to France with his father."

It pleased her to have him so happy, and when the time came for him to leave, she tried to be brave. But tears came to her eyes.

"It breaks my heart to see you go," she said. "But I know you'll do well, Stephen, wherever you are."

Stephen smiled down at her. "I'll do my best to make you proud of me," he promised, gripping her hands in his. Then, turning, he ran down the steps and started for the docks.

Aboard the frigate *United States,* he found his good friends Richard Somers, who was a midshipman, and Charles Stewart, who was a lieutenant. They welcomed him with loud cries and much clapping on the shoulder.

"It'll be like the old days at Dr. Abercrombie's academy," Richard said.

"Except now I'm the leader instead of Stephen," Charles declared with a wide grin. And he pointed to the lieutenant's epaulet on his left shoulder. "Before Captain Barry and I are through with you midshipmen, you'll be able to hit a silver dollar on the mast of a ship a mile away. The captain is a great one for good marksmanship."

"Don't I know it!" Stephen exclaimed. "He's always talking to my father about making every shot count and not wasting ammunition."

"Well, Mr. Somers," Charles said grandly, "show Midshipman Decatur to his quarters in the steerage."

"Steerage?" asked Stephen, surprised.

"Certainly," replied Charles. "You didn't think that midshipmen were on the same deck with us lieutenants, did you?"

"I don't know what I thought," Stephen answered ruefully. He trailed Richard down ladders almost to the bottom of the ship. And there in the darkness, lighted by a few candle lanterns, he was given a hammock and space for his sea chest.

"This is like being in the hold with the cargo," observed Stephen.

"Don't worry," advised Richard. "You only come down here to eat and sleep. And you'll be so tired when you go to bed that you could sleep curled up in a barrel with a porcupine on each side of you."

After the *United States* and the *Delaware* with Stephen's father in command, had been at sea only a short time, Stephen understood exactly what Richard meant.

He had to learn all about the ship with its endless masts, wire, yards, chain, rope, lines, and sails. He learned how to get under way. To sail with the wind. To sail against the wind. To sail in fair weather and foul.

And besides working ship it was drill, drill, drill in gunnery. Captain Barry kept them practicing at the guns night and day. They fired at targets in the sunlight. At night they shot by the gleam of battle lanterns. They set off the guns in the fog, the rain, the wind. Guns on the *United States* flashed in the darkness. At other times, the smoke of their powder rose like clouds in the starlight.

Stephen became one of the best marksmen aboard. Captain Barry praised him. And even the stern, hot-tempered third lieutenant, James Barron, complimented him now and then.

Stephen loved life on the ship. He wrote his mother glowing letters. The hard work and the drilling challenged him each day to become stronger and more skillful.

And he even took the jokes played on the new midshipmen like himself with good humor. He never got ruffled when his shipmates teased him for being a greenhorn.

Sometimes the *Delaware*, which was commanded by Stephen's father, cruised with the *United States*. Before long, Congress appointed Barry the commodore of this little fleet. He was ordered to capture French armed vessels wherever he found them. Barry felt that American ships near the West Indies were in the greatest danger from the French. So the *United States* and the *Delaware* sailed southeast toward those islands.

The two frigates cruised about for weeks. Not a Frenchman did they find. And not a single American merchant ship did they hear of in trouble.

Stephen and Richard and Charles were disgusted. They wanted to see some real naval action after their long "practice fighting."

Commodore Barry counseled, "Patience. And keep your eyes peeled." He would stroke his big nose thoughtfully. "There are bound to be armed Frenchmen lurking hereabouts. It stands to reason, they'll try to keep ships from trading with the British West Indies."

Stephen and his friends scanned the sea and watched impatiently for craft armed with batteries of guns.

New Year's Day of 1799 had come and gone when at last they sighted their first French privateers.

Stephen heard Commodore Barry cry,

"General quarters!" And as he ran to join his gun crew, he saw his father on the quarter-deck of the *Delaware*. Captain Decatur was shouting the same order through his trumpet to his men: "General quarters!" Then Stephen heard the roll of the drums on both ships.

Moving swiftly, he helped his crew remove the gun covers. The gunport was raised. With a rumbling of wheels, the nine-foot cannon was run out. The various crews were so well trained, they worked with the precision of clocks. Within a few minutes, all forty-four guns on the frigate were ready.

Stephen watched the two French ships come closer. With bright flags flying and sails billowing in the wind, they advanced toward the Americans. Their guns began to roar as soon as they were within range of the frigates.

"Why they're nothing but overgrown catboats!" Stephen murmured disappointedly. "And here they come spitting at us."

Alert, he and his crew waited for the commodore's order. A second later it came: "Fire!"

Once, twice the Americans fired. Down

came the flags in surrender on the French privateers. The fight had scarcely started before it was over. Some of the Americans jeered at the Frenchmen for being cowards.

That evening, Barry invited the midshipmen to the main cabin for supper. He praised them for their skillful, accurate gunnery.

"You shot well," he said, "and the ships were so badly damaged, they could neither fight nor get away. But I want you to remember something." He paused to be sure he had the attention of everyone at the table.

"It was no disgrace for the Frenchmen to surrender," he continued. "Their ships are smaller than ours. They have only sixteen guns on one and fourteen on the other. We have forty-four guns on each of our frigates. Our frigates were built to whip anything except the largest battleship. We with our forty-four guns may come up against a seventy-four-gun warship some day. Then will come the test of our courage."

Stephen's and Richard's glances met across the table. Both of them were eager for this test. But Barry was speaking again and they turned to listen.

"In my opinion, we aren't likely to encounter any French warships," the commodore went on. "Most of them are engaged in battles with the British. This frigate is a match for any smaller craft we may meet. So is the *Delaware*. For this reason we are parting company. By cruising separately, we can cover a wider area."

Stephen stirred uneasily. Although he could not talk with his father every day, he knew he was always close by on the *Delaware*. It was a comforting thought. And now . . .

"Mr. Decatur. Mr. Decatur!"

Stephen raised his head to look at Commodore Barry. "Yes, sir," he said. "I'm sorry, sir."

Barry smiled. "Go and order the officer of the deck to hoist the signal for Captain Decatur to come aboard," he said. "The captain and I must map out our cruising grounds. And you and your father can have a visit before our ships go their separate ways." He rose from the table, dismissing the other midshipmen.

After a long visit with his father later that night, Stephen climbed into his hammock. He felt grateful to the commodore for giving him a chance to have a last talk with his father.

"But the commodore thinks of everyone," Stephen thought. He knew that Barry had given every seaman who had a relative on the *Delaware* a chance to say good-by. No wonder men and officers alike admired him and wanted to do their best for their commander.

By morning the *Delaware* was gone. The *United States* headed toward the British-owned island of Martinique. There, on February 3, Commodore Barry sighted a vessel behaving very suspiciously. With every sail set to catch the wind, she was slipping swiftly past between the *United States* and the island's shore.

From close by the quarter-deck, Stephen observed her curiously. It was easy to see that she was trying to sneak away from the Americans. And she was a French privateer. A moment later the men aboard the frigate were ordered to give chase. Stephen dashed over to join his crew. They loaded the gun.

The *United States* crowded up to the French vessel. She came about, swerving to starboard, in an effort to escape.

Stephen's crew was ordered, "Fire your gun!"

There was a roar. The single well-placed shot struck the hull of the privateer, piercing the ship through and through. Water rushed in and the vessel began to sink. It looked as though the men aboard her would surely be drowned.

"Man the boats!" Barry commanded instantly.

Stephen with his crew leaped to one of the boats and lowered it. They were the first to

reach the sinking craft. All was chaos aboard the privateer. Crews had abandoned their guns. Officers were shouting meaningless orders. Sailors were jumping into the sea.

Stephen and his men rowed around, hauling them out of the water and into their boat. The other boats from the *United States* joined them in the rescue.

The last to jump from the ship was the French captain. Seeing him, Stephen rowed over and dragged him to safety.

"I didn't know you Americans were at war with France," growled the French captain ungraciously in broken but understandable English.

Without pausing in his work of rescuing others, Stephen called over his shoulder. "We are not at war with France, sir," he said. "But you French are sinking *our* ships and imprisoning *our* crews. Now we are going to protect ourselves, sir, that is all."

The French captain said no more. He knew the young American spoke the truth.

The Americans saved almost all the men who had been on the ship. Then the *United States* continued to cruise in the West Indies with the Frenchmen aboard as prisoners.

When groups of French prisoners were brought up on deck for exercise, they took particular interest in Midshipman Decatur. Lean, strong, and graceful as a steel rapier, he was full of fire and energy. He was as skilled with sails and guns as any seasoned mariner. He was well liked by all the officers. And each man in the crew looked upon him as a friend.

One day a group of them saw something that neither they nor anyone aboard ever forgot.

The *United States* had been hove to near islands where sharp coral reefs rose close to the surface of the water. A stiff wind blew up suddenly. Fearing the frigate might be blown upon the reefs, Barry ordered the crew to set sail. The frigate would go farther out to sea.

No sooner were the sails unfurled, however, than a sailor called from the mast top.

"Man overboard!" he shouted.

"Let go the buoy!" the officer of the deck cried to the life-buoy watchman. "First boat away! Second boat away! Third boat away!" he commanded the lifeboat crews.

Stephen, who was on deck, had heard the cry of "man overboard." He ran to the side and climbed up the ratlines. Looking down, he saw the upflung hand of the drowning seaman. He measured the distance to the water. Then he dived. With swift strokes he swam to the man and quickly rolled him over on his back. Supporting him with one arm and swimming with the other arm and his legs, Stephen made for the frigate.

He soon discovered he was gaining no headway. The waves pushed him farther and farther away from the ship. He gave up struggling against them. Instead, he conserved his strength. Treading water, he paddled just enough to keep himself and the unconscious seaman afloat.

The ship seemed a long way off. The men in the rigging were mere dots. He could see

He measured the distance to the water and dived

the boats nowhere. But he knew the crews were out on the water there, searching for him. Before many minutes had passed, he glimpsed one of the boats.

"Boat ahoy!" he shouted.

The boat appeared to walk on the water toward him, as the men dipped their oars, pulling with hard, quick, even strokes. Then hands reached out and lifted the sailor and Stephen over the side.

When they reached the frigate, the half-drowned man was put in the care of the surgeon. As Stephen climbed to the deck, Charles Stewart and Richard Somers were the first to greet him.

"You're even a better swimmer than you used to be when we swam in the Delaware River!" they told him.

The commodore hurried up to thank Stephen.

Then Stephen dodged through the crowd of sailors to go below to change his wet clothes. The men watched him, their eyes filled with admiration and something deeper than that —respect and trust.

As for the French prisoners—when they

had returned to their quarters, they talked about what they had seen.

"This navy the Americans are building—it is a fine one," they told one another. "Their warships are well designed. And how well disciplined their men are! Do you see how the officers and men respect each other? Why, even the life of a poor seaman is considered valuable and important."

CHAPTER EIGHT

Convoy Duty

BEFORE long the little United States Navy had proved to the French that wherever American ships sailed, they would be protected. So the French left American ships alone and there was peace between the two countries.

Stephen's father had been made the commander of a fine new frigate, the *Philadelphia*. But now he felt that the time had come when he should resign.

"The Navy can do without old men like me," Captain Decatur told his wife. "If old men leave the service, there will be places in a peacetime navy for the young men."

Mrs. Decatur shook her head fondly at her husband. "I don't know what you'll do without a ship," she said.

"We'll move to our place, Mount Airy, and I shall be a country gentleman," he replied gaily.

So it was to Mount Airy, ten miles outside Philadelphia, that Stephen came one afternoon late in May. His brother James was with him. The young Decaturs were riding in a carriage which they had hired in Philadelphia. When it stopped under the portico, Stephen hopped out.

"Wait, please," he told the driver. "We'll be going back to the city in an hour."

"Anybody home?" called James, running up the steps. "Mother! Father! John!"

In a moment, Mrs. Decatur appeared in the doorway. "My!" she exclaimed and held out her arms to them. "You're noisy enough for a whole navy."

"Where are Father and John?" Stephen asked as he gave his mother a hug. "We haven't much time."

Mrs. Decature stood off and proudly regarded her tall sons. How fine they looked in their uniforms! Stephen, who was twenty-two, had a single epaulet on his shoulder to show that he was now a lieutenant. And James, who had joined the navy about a year before, seemed very grown up in his midshipman's red and blue.

"Not much time? Why?" she asked.

"Because the fleet's leaving for the Mediterranean Sea tomorrow morning with Commodore Dale as commander in chief," answered Stephen.

"Now, when did all this happen?" inquired Captain Decatur, entering the hall with John.

"The fleet's sailing? Tomorrow?" exclaimed John.

"That's what the boys said," the captain replied. "Come, let's go some place where we can talk." He led his two sailor sons into the living room.

As soon as they were all seated, Stephen began. "It's because of the Barbary pirates," he said. "They're making trouble again."

Captain Decatur nodded gravely. The Barbary pirates had been making trouble for more than three hundred years. These pirates came from four small countries on the north coast of Africa—Morocco, Tunis, Tripoli, and Algiers. They had captured countless ships flying the flags of many nations. Some of the nations paid the rulers of the four Barbary states to let their ships sail in peace.

"So-o," said Captain Decatur slowly, looking at his tall young sons, "you two are off to fight the pirates!"

"It looks that way," Stephen said happily. "They've asked the United States for bribes, but President Jefferson has refused to pay them. He's sending the fleet to the Mediterranean to protect all American ships."

There was silence after he stopped speaking. They were thinking about the important step the Government was taking. For the first time, an American fleet was being sent to the Mediterranean to protect Americans at sea.

In a moment, they all began talking at once about other things. They tried to be as cheerful and gay as if Stephen and James were sailing down the Delaware and not to the far-off Barbary Coast of Africa.

"I wish your sister and her two boys could see you before you go," Mrs. Decatur finally said.

"I do, too," Stephen replied, getting up. "But we haven't time. We must go now. Come on, James."

They hurried out to the waiting carriage. The driver slapped the reins against his horse. The brothers called their last good-by's to the family. The carriage turned off the driveway and onto the road to Philadelphia.

Before the sun had set, the two brothers were again at the wharves. There they parted. James rowed out to his ship with a group of other midshipmen. And Stephen went aboard the frigate *Essex,* where he was assigned as first lieutenant to Captain William Bainbridge. It was a new assignment and his old friends, Somers and Stewart, were no longer among his shipmates.

The fleet put to sea about dawn the next morning. It crossed the Atlantic Ocean and reached the Rock of Gibraltar, the entrance to the Mediterranean, one month later, on July 1, 1801.

Almost at once reports of trouble with pirates from Tripoli were brought to the fleet.

On the *Essex* Decatur was walking the quarter-deck. He could hear the commander in chief, Commodore Richard Dale, and Captain Bainbridge discussing plans for action in the captain's cabin.

Soon the commodore left and Captain Bainbridge came to the door. "Please step in here, Lieutenant Decatur," he said.

Decatur went inside the little cabin. The captain began to talk in his usual crisp way.

"Commodore Dale will take the other ships to cruise along the north African shore," he told Decatur. "The *Essex* will sail alone along the south coasts of France and Spain. We are to round up all homeward-bound American vessels and convoy them out of the Mediterranean. Set the course for France, Lieutenant."

Decatur saluted. "Aye, aye, sir," he said and returned to the deck. "Set sail," he ordered the crew. Then he gave directions to the helmsman for sailing east and north to France.

Running his eye over the frigate and the well-trained crew, Decatur decided that any nation might well be proud of so fine a man-of-war. As first lieutenant he was responsible for the work of the ship, the discipline of the men, and the navigation. Because he tried hard to be the best officer possible, the *Essex* was known throughout the fleet as a "happy ship."

As she sailed along the coast, the *Essex* picked up one American merchant vessel after another. She guarded them as a mother hen does her chickens. And all went smoothly until she neared the port of Barcelona in Spain.

The Spaniards had a big ship, called a xebec, guarding the harbor. The xebec was a long, low ship with huge, white curving sails and it was the pride of the Spanish Navy.

Then into the harbor glided the American Navy frigate *Essex*. She floated in under a cloud of snowy sails, with flags flying and her paint gleaming in the hot, coppery sunshine. Her officers and crew looked very smart and

[*89*]

trim in their spotless American uniforms. She was a beautiful sight as she came to anchor with a string of merchant ships in her wake. In comparison the xebec seemed inferior.

From the taffrail, Decatur saw people running down to the sea wall with its towering monument to Christopher Columbus. They were pointing out the big, strange ship to one another. Men and boys were scrambling into sailboats and rowboats and pushing out into the harbor. Soon, in the water around the frigate were clusters of boats. And the air was filled with the musical voices of Spaniards exclaiming over the wonderful ship.

"It seems we've caused a sensation, sir," Decatur remarked to Captain Bainbridge, who was standing beside him.

"It's probably the first time that any of them have seen an American warship," the captain pointed out. He turned aside to gaze at the xebec which lay not far away. "The captain of that Spanish Navy ship is very interested in us, too," he observed.

Decatur followed his glance. The Spanish captain was inspecting the *Essex* through a spyglass.

Bainbridge turned back to Decatur. "You had better go ashore with a crew for fresh provisions," he told him. "And arrange for a supply of food. We'll need new stores before convoying the ships down the coast and out into the Atlantic Ocean."

"Yes, sir. I'll go right away," Decatur said. Descending the short ladder to the deck, he ordered a mate, "Man the longboat. Smartly now."

When the longboat was lowered, he climbed down the ladder and seated himself in the stern. Blue-shirted fishermen with purple caps, and boys in black suits and red stocking caps brought their boats closer. They stared curiously at the Americans.

"Pull for shore," Decatur called to his men.

The longboat skimmed over the water trailed by a crowd of Spaniards. They surrounded the Americans all the way to the sea wall at the foot of the Rambla, the city's widest, longest boulevard.

Decatur and his crew went ashore. In the big open markets they found oranges and figs, pomegranates, goats' milk cheese, olives, berries, fish, and piles of green vegetables. By

[*91*]

evening Decatur had visited many merchants and had arranged for coffee, flour, salt, as well as other staples, to be delivered by market boats to the *Essex*. And the longboat had been loaded with fresh vegetables and fruits.

It was dark when Decatur and his crew started back. Once again the crew dipped their oars. The longboat swept out into the harbor. They picked their way among the big and little craft on the water, guided by swaying lights at their masts. The Americans were no longer followed. But they were watched with keen interest.

The Spanish xebec was agleam with the red-yellow glow of whale-oil lanterns. As De-

catur drew nearer, he could see the officers on the quarter-deck. They were handsomely clothed in uniforms decorated with much gold braid and lace. They strode up and down, with their heads high, as though they held the rest of the world in contempt.

When he heard the splashing of the longboat's oars, the Spanish captain looked over the taffrail. After regarding the Americans for a bit, he called out an order. Suddenly a puff of smoke sprang from the xebec. A shot whizzed across the longboat's bow and fell into the water.

"Shall we heave to, sir?" the young coxswain asked Decatur. "The Spaniards fired

that shot as a signal for us to stop and be recognized. Didn't they, sir?"

"They did," answered Decatur angrily. "Pay no attention. Keep on rowing," he told the crew. "The Spaniards are treating us like common sea dogs. Trying to impress us with how important they are and how unimportant we are. But they'll soon find they can't treat officers and men of the United States Navy that way."

As soon as the longboat reached the *Essex,* Decatur left word that the provisions were to be turned over to the steward. Then he went at once to Captain Bainbridge to report what had happened. The captain was furious.

"With your permission," Decatur said, "I'm going aboard the xebec tomorrow and demand an apology."

"Permission granted," Bainbridge instantly replied.

The next morning, in full dress uniform, Decatur presented himself on board the xebec.

"First Lieutenant Stephen Decatur of the United States Navy frigate *Essex,*" he announced to the officer of the deck. "Please tell your captain I wish to see him."

The Spaniard looked sharply at the stern, handsome young American. He was certainly not a young man to be treated lightly. The Spaniard bowed stiffly from the waist.

"I regret to inform the lieutenant that the captain is ashore," he said politely. He spoke in the very correct English he had learned from the British at Gibraltar.

"Then tell him when he returns," Decatur replied, "that he fired on my boat last night. And I call him a cowardly scoundrel. When we meet on shore, I'll cut his ears off."

With that Decatur spun round on his heel. He climbed below to the gig, which was waiting for him at the foot of the ship's ladder.

In no time a storm began over what the Spaniards declared was an insult to their captain. The captain-general of the province complained to the American consul in Barcelona. Captain Bainbridge sent a letter explaining what had happened, to the American Minister at Madrid. And the American Minister took the matter to Spain's Minister of State. He reported the whole affair to the King of Spain.

In a short time, His Majesty the King sent a royal order to the captain of the xebec and

[95]

to all other commanders in the Spanish Navy. And a letter from the King was brought to the *Essex* for Captain Bainbridge.

Decatur and the other officers of the *Essex* were summoned at once to Bainbridge's cabin. Although Decatur felt he had acted rightly in resenting the insult to the United States Navy, he was worried. What would the King of Spain say? What was he going to do about the Americans?

Young Lieutenant Decatur stood quietly with the others before the captain, but there was dread in his heart.

Bainbridge picked up the letter from his table and began to read it aloud. The King apologized for the behavior of the captain of the xebec! Then the King excused him by saying that the Spanish officer was simply over-eager to increase the honor of Spain. But, so there would be no further misunderstanding, a royal order had been issued.

"The officers of the United States are to be treated with courtesy and respect at all times," the order stated. "Especially those attached to the frigate *Essex*."

Decatur could have shouted with relief.

"Well, gentlemen," remarked the captain. "Little by little the United States is gaining the respect of other nations. First, France. Now, Spain. Lieutenant Decatur, you are to be commended for the part you've had in bringing honor to your country."

CHAPTER NINE

Sent Home

THE United States frigate *New York* rode at anchor in the still harbor waters of the island of Malta in the Mediterranean. It was past twelve o'clock of a January night. There was a full moon overhead.

Decatur was alone on deck. After a little more than a year of convoy duty, he had been transferred to the *New York* as first lieutenant. Under his new captain, James Barron, he had had to work doubly hard to train a green crew and keep the frigate shipshape. Captain Barron was not well liked. And the job of keeping men and ship working smoothly all seemed to fall on Decatur.

It was not unusual for him to be on deck at midnight. Tonight he had allowed a group of midshipmen to go ashore to attend a play at the theatre in Malta. He was taking the anchor watch for one of them. The shore party was due back at one.

Decatur saw the lights go out in Captain Barron's cabin. The captain had gone to bed.

After a while, Decatur strolled forward along one side of the deck. All was quiet at the fore end of the ship. Only the snores of sleeping sailors could be heard as he passed the companionway to the deck below.

Continuing aft on the other side of the deck, he came to the rope ladder. It had been left hanging over the side until the return of the midshipmen. Leaning his elbows on the rail, Decatur paused to look up at the steep, narrow streets, the flat-roofed buildings, and the high rocky ledges of the island fortress.

Then, in the bright moonlight, he saw a group of men striding down one of the steep streets. When they reached the shore, they stopped to argue about something. Decatur recognized them as the Americans from the *New York*. After a few minutes, they climbed into their boat and shoved off.

Decatur waited for them at the top of the

ladder. Very soon the boat thumped against the ship. Then he could hear the men talking in low, bitter voices.

"Blamed lobsterback snobs!" one of the midshipmen muttered.

"Should have beaten the tar out of that whole lot of pickle-faced, high-and-mighty Britishers," declared another.

Decatur put his head over the rail. "What's the matter?" he asked in an ordinary tone.

"Had a fight, sir," answered a midshipman. "Has Captain Barron turned in, Lieutenant?"

"Yes," replied Decatur. "There's no one on deck."

"We're in luck," the midshipman told his friends. "It's Lieutenant Decatur. He's alone." The midshipman started up the ladder with the others after him.

"What happened?" Decatur asked when all of them were aboard.

Midshipman Joseph Bainbridge, who was the younger brother of Decatur's captain on the *Essex,* stepped forward.

"I took a swing, sir, at Mr. Cochran, secretary to the Governor of Malta. And I knocked him down, sir," he said.

[*100*]

"What do you mean? Just now?" Decatur asked.

"Yes, sir. Just now in the theatre lobby," Bainbridge explained. "Cochran kept jostling me. I held my temper at first. But when he jostled me the third time, I hit him."

"Let me explain, sir," interrupted another midshipman. "We were sitting next to some British officers. This Mr. Cochran was one of them. Well, the British began talking about the cowardly Yankees. Said we were afraid of the smell of gunpowder. That we'd never dare go out and fight the Barbary pirates."

Another midshipman spoke up. "So we got up and left."

"And they followed us out into the lobby," continued the first midshipman. "It was rather crowded. And Cochran started to jostle Bainbridge, making fun of him."

"All right," Decatur said. "But what happened after Bainbridge knocked him down?"

"Nothing, sir," Bainbridge said. "People were dumbfounded that anyone would have the nerve to hit one of their precious British officers. We left. That was all."

"I'm afraid that may not be the end of it," returned Decatur. "But go to your quarters. And on your way," he said to one of the midshipman, "rouse the first gunner's mate to take over your watch."

The group went below. Decatur waited for the gunner's mate. He turned over the watch to him and told him to haul in the ladder. Then Decatur went to his stateroom. He was worried about young Bainbridge. The British seemed to feel themselves superior to most other people since they had won the war with France. Some of them looked down particularly on the "upstart" Americans. For an American midshipman to strike the Governor's secretary was bound to cause serious trouble. The fact that Bainbridge had been bullied into punching Mr. Cochran would be overlooked. Decatur did not sleep soundly that night.

The following morning, Decatur was on the quarter-deck when young Bainbridge came up. The midshipman was white-faced and tense. He saluted smartly.

"Could I show you something, sir?" he asked. He thrust out a sheet of paper.

Decatur read the note written on it. Mr. Cochran challenged Midshipman Joseph Bainbridge to a duel with pistols. Decatur's fists clenched in anger. "Do you realize this man is an expert pistol shot?" he asked.

"Yes, sir," Bainbridge answered. "Everyone in Malta knows it."

"And I know you're not an expert with a pistol," Decatur snapped. "You'll be killed."

"But I have to answer the challenge," Bainbridge declared. "I'd disgrace the United States Navy if I didn't."

"I know," agreed Decatur. "Not to accept

[*103*]

a challenge to a duel is considered contemptible. But let me be your second and set the conditions."

Bainbridge was relieved and honored. He accepted Decatur's offer gratefully.

At once, Mr. Cochran was informed that his challenge was accepted. The duel was arranged for the next day at an out-of-way place near the city.

Mr. Cochran and his friend, and the two Americans met the following day as agreed. Bainbridge appeared cool, although his face was drawn and pale. Mr. Cochran was completely self-confident.

"Pistols at four paces," Decatur told Cochran's friend.

"But Mr. Cochran is—" began the other.

"Yes, I know," Decatur interrupted him. "Mr. Cochran is an expert duelist. Mr. Bainbridge is not. Therefore, we make the conditions."

"Very well," agreed the other.

Bainbridge and Cochran each took a pistol from the case which Cochran's friend had brought. They faced each other, then walked backwards four long steps.

"Take aim. Fire!" Decatur cried.

Cochran, as an expert duelist, was used to firing at ten paces. He missed Bainbridge entirely. Bainbridge's shot went through the secretary's hat.

Both Bainbridge and Decatur were willing to consider the duel ended. But the Englishmen were not satisfied. Cochran angrily demanded another round.

Decatur drew Bainbridge aside. "I realize we, as American Navy men, will be considered cowards, if we don't go on with this. But you can refuse."

"I can't refuse to go on, sir," Bainbridge declared gravely. "I wouldn't be living up to the code of honor among Army and Navy men all over the world, if I backed out now." He shook his head. "No, sir, I won't back out."

"Then aim lower, if you don't want to be killed," Decatur warned him.

Once again Bainbridge and Cochran took their places. They fired. The Englishman toppled over, shot between the eyes. Bainbridge was untouched.

Sadly the two Americans returned to their ship. Bainbridge had defended the honor of the United States Navy. Decatur had upheld him. But they were not happy over the duel.

In a very short time, the Governor of Malta heard all about it. His secretary had been killed and he was determined that the Americans should be punished. He demanded that Decatur and Bainbridge be brought to trial.

Commodore Morris of the United States fleet considered the matter. Mr. Cochran had offended the Americans first. He had made the challenge. The commodore refused to allow Decatur and Bainbridge to be tried in the English courts. But he sent word to the Gov-

ernor that he would relieve the young men of duty and send them back home with a report.

On April 7, 1803, Decatur and young Bainbridge sailed away from Malta on the *Chesapeake,* bound for New York. They stood side by side on deck, gazing out across the sea. What lay ahead of them? Decatur was filled with dread. When he reached the United States he might be dismissed from the Navy in disgrace. Bainbridge wondered anxiously if he, too, might not be dismissed in disgrace. Both of them thought gloomily of the long, weary miles across the ocean to New York.

CHAPTER TEN

The Terrible Commodore

Six months later, Decatur was anxiously pacing the deck of the brig *Argus*. The ship was long overdue in Gibraltar, and he was worried. Commodore Edward Preble was the new commander of the Mediterranean fleet of the United States. He was not only the strictest officer in the Navy, but he was also one of the hottest tempered.

Decatur remembered how he and Bainbridge had paced the deck of the *Chesapeake* when they were being sent home. How worried they had been then! And, as it turned out, all their worry had been for nothing. By the time they had reached New York, the Governor of Malta had changed his mind about who was to blame for the death of Mr. Cochran. He had learned that Mr. Cochran had first stirred up trouble and then insisted on a duel. So he had suggested that the matter be dropped.

The officials of the United States Navy had not reprimanded either Decatur or Bainbridge. And now Decatur was taking a new brig across the ocean to Gibraltar to join the rest of the fleet.

It seemed to him, as he paced the deck of the *Argus,* that everything had gone wrong from the beginning. Certain equipment was lacking for the brig. He had to wait for that. There was no crew. He had had to recruit men. Then he had to lay in a great quantity of supplies. For he could not depend upon obtaining anything in Gibraltar. Delay. Delay. Delay. And the Atlantic crossing in the new brig had been unusually rough. More delay because of bad weather. Decatur should have arrived in September. It was now the end of October.

He quit tramping up and down the *Argus's* deck. He stopped to look up at the red cliffs of St. Vincent on the Portugal coast. They stood out sharply against the bright blue sky.

"Well," he mused, "with any luck at all, I'll bring the *Argus* into Gibraltar by tomorrow, the first of November." He tried not to think about how angry Commodore Preble might be because he was so late.

The *Argus* reached Gibraltar the next morning. Decatur anchored in the harbor where already all the other ships of the United States fleet were gathered. After putting on a fresh uniform, Decatur ordered the gig manned. As the crew rowed toward the flagship *Constitution,* he reviewed in his mind the report that he would make to the commodore.

"Deck there! Officer coming aboard!" shouted the coxswain, steering the gig alongside the big ship.

Decatur grabbed the rope ladder which was dropped over the rail, and climbed up. A lean-faced officer met him.

"Lieutenant Stephen Decatur of the *Argus*, reporting to Commodore Preble," Decatur informed him.

"I'm Commodore Preble," said a spare, dignified figure stepping in front of the deck officer. "Come with me." He briskly led the way to his cabin.

Once they were inside, Preble said, "So you're young Decatur." He narrowed his eyes at the twenty-four-year-old commander of the *Argus*. "I expected you three weeks ago." He then stared at Decatur, who stood respectfully but confidently in front of him. "Well, let's have your report, Lieutenant," he snapped.

Decatur began at once. He made no excuses. He stuck to facts. He told very simply what had happened since he had been given the command of the *Argus*. His report was short and to the point.

After it was finished, Decatur expected an

outburst of temper from Preble. Instead, the commodore said nothing. He again studied Decatur from head to foot. He noted the poised body, the firm jaw, the clear, direct glance.

"Looks as alert as a young eagle," Preble thought. He smiled sourly and waved Decatur to a chair beside the chart table. "Sit down," he invited.

"You're my man, I think," went on the commodore when they were both seated. "I need someone to command the schooner *Enterprise*. She's a very handy little craft. Can go closer to the shore than any of our other vessels. I'm going to patrol the waters near Tripoli. You can help me. We'll blockade the port. No vessels allowed in. No vessels allowed out. We're going to find out how much we can hurt the pirates with a blockade."

Decatur drew a long breath of relief. His spirits rose. The commodore evidently was not going to rebuke him for being late. Indeed, Preble seemed to like him. On his part, Decatur felt almost friendly toward the snappish, disagreeable-looking man.

"Sounds as though there'd be some action,"

Decatur said eagerly. "If so, I certainly am your man, sir."

"Thought as much," agreed Preble. "You won't have time to waste settling personal quarrels, I can tell you. Want you to remember a Navy man's honor rests upon how well he behaves in military action. Not in obeying stupid rules of conduct, like dueling." He rose. "You'll take over the *Enterprise* at once and be ready to sail when I leave on the *Constitution*."

Decatur was very cheerful when he left. He and the commodore seemed to "hit it off." The remark Preble had made about conduct —well, it made Decatur think. Perhaps settling quarrels by dueling was not a very good code of honor to follow after all.

Decatur was pleased with his new assignment as commander of the *Enterprise*. A little more than a week after he had cast anchor at Gibraltar, he was at sea again. He had sailed ahead of the *Constitution* in order to convoy a cargo ship to the United States Naval base at Syracuse on the island of Sicily. The *Constitution* caught up with him. And the three ships went into Syracuse together.

[*113*]

As soon as they were moored, Preble called Decatur aboard the *Constitution*. The commander had very bad news. The big Navy frigate *Philadelphia* had run aground on the reefs at Tripoli. She had been captured by Tripolitan pirates before the Americans could get her afloat again.

"We must sail for Tripoli immediately," Preble said. "We'll have to reconnoiter the harbor and the defenses. We must find out if there is any way of recapturing the *Philadelphia*."

The *Enterprise* and the *Constitution* weighed anchor and sped southward toward the African coast. As they drew near Tripoli, Decatur took the lead. He could sail closer to shore than the other ship. But it was a dangerous region. There were sharp reefs to avoid as well as Barbary pirates. Their ships might be waiting in any of the little harbors or narrow inlets to make a surprise attack.

Decatur was taking no chances. "Turn all hands out," he ordered his first lieutenant.

While the schooner's gun crews were forming around their cannon, Decatur climbed up the shrouds. Through his spyglass, he exam-

Through his spyglass he examined the sea all around

ined the sea all around. Sure enough, there was a boat headed toward the *Enterprise*. She was a ketch—a small gunboat—from Tripoli.

Decatur returned to the deck. "Beat the men to quarters," he ordered.

The boatswain's pipe shrilled. The gunports were raised and the cannon run out. Sail after sail was cracked on the schooner. She flew over the water, cutting off the ketch. The gunboat came up into the wind and lay rocking helplessly under the guns of the *Enterprise*.

Without a shot having been fired by either vessel, the captain of the ketch hauled down his flag in surrender.

"Prepare to receive a boarding party," Decatur shouted through his cupped hands.

A few minutes later, a joyful yell went up on the *Enterprise* as the party of Americans clambered over the ketch's rail. It made Decatur happy to hear them cheering. The ketch was not much of a prize. But she was the first. And there was no telling how important the little gunboat might prove to be.

CHAPTER ELEVEN

"*Americanos!*"

THE *Constitution*, the *Enterprise*, and the little ketch sailed slowly toward Tripoli. Although it was the middle of the morning, the December day was dark. A raw northeast wind sent clouds scudding overhead. And the cold blue water of the Mediterranean was rough and speckled with whitecaps.

At first the land looked like a ragged trail of smoke. Then gradually the hills and the rocky coast came into sight. Soon the Americans could see towers rising above the city's walls. The palace of the Bashaw who ruled Tripoli loomed up just beyond the harbor where ships were moored. Near this stone castle was a great fortress.

It was Decatur who first sighted the *Phila-*

[*117*]

delphia. She was the biggest ship in the harbor. She was within range of the guns of the castle and the fortress. And all about were Tripolitan cruisers and gunboats. The Bashaw of Tripoli was guarding his great prize well.

Decatur called across to Commodore Preble on the *Constitution.* "I've picked up the *Philadelphia,* sir," he said. He pointed her out to the commodore.

Decatur saw the commodore swing his telescope to bear on the ship. One of her masts was gone. She had been stripped of her sails and damaged by battering on the rocks. Altogether she was too crippled to sail. She would have to be hauled away by another vessel.

The sight of the gallant warship that his father had once commanded stirred Decatur deeply. He could not bear to think that the pirates of Tripoli would use this American ship to fight against Americans. In spite of the pirates and their guns, the *Philadelphia* must be recaptured or destroyed. He must talk with the commodore.

Going aboard the *Constitution,* he hurried aft to the quarter-deck. Commodore Preble stood scowling at the sky.

He grunted as Decatur came up. "There's dirty weather knocking about," he grumbled.

"Yes, sir," Decatur agreed, saluting smartly. "But I've come to offer to take the *Enterprise* into Tripoli now, sir. If I can't tow the *Philadelphia* out, I'll set fire to her."

Preble looked at his young lieutenant for a moment, still scowling. "We've lost the *Philadelphia* on the rocks," he snapped. "I don't propose to lose the *Enterprise*. She's too big to make it through that narrow harbor entrance in a gale. I'll keep your offer in mind, though, and give the matter some thought. Now, if you'll return to your ship, Lieutenant, we'll put back for Syracuse."

"Aye, sir," Decatur said. But as he climbed down the ladder to his gig, he thought, "Back to Syracuse without firing a shot. Confound the man. He's too cautious!"

The three vessels lifted anchor. They worked their way northward to the island of Sicily in the face of a lashing gale and pounding seas.

When they were once more in the quiet port of Syracuse, the commodore began to consider the matter of the *Philadelphia*. The

[*119*]

frigate must be destroyed before the pirates could repair her. The question was how to do it without risking the loss of another ship.

The commodore discussed one idea after another with Decatur. For many nights they talked across the table in the big square cabin of the *Constitution.*

"Sir, I could sneak in with some men on that little ketch we captured," Decatur said one evening. "I can see now, sir, it would have been foolish to go into Tripoli with the *Enterprise.* And we can't get past the pirates' gunboats with any of our smaller vessels either. They'd recognize us. But if we use the ketch —that's different. She's one of their own boats. They wouldn't be suspicious."

The commodore glanced up into Decatur's gleaming eyes. The lieutenant was only twenty-four. Yet he could be as level-headed as an old ship's captain at times. Added to that he had courage, a fiery spirit, and a fine way of handling men.

"If you've a plan, I'd like to hear it," Preble said.

Decatur then told how he thought he could take the ketch into the harbor and burn the

[*120*]

Philadelphia. They talked about it for a long time. Preble in his thorough, painstaking way, examined what was good about the plan and what was bad. He considered how it could be carried out, step by step.

Finally he said, "Fit out the ketch. I'll give you written orders shortly."

"Aye, sir," Decatur answered. Leaving the cabin, he felt he was walking on clouds. He—Stephen Decatur—was going to lead an expedition against the Barbary pirates!

At once he set men to work on the ketch. She was made ready to put to sea. And she was loaded with combustibles—all the things that make a quick, hot fire.

On the morning of February 3, Decatur received his orders from Preble to take command of the ketch and sail to Tripoli.

"I shall send you midshipmen from the *Constitution,*" wrote the commodore. "And you will take seventy men, including officers, from the *Enterprise.* You will be ready to sail tomorrow evening."

That afternoon Decatur stood on the quarter-deck of the *Enterprise* and ordered his boatswain to pipe all hands aft. As soon as the shuffle of the sailors' bare feet and the scrape of officers' boots had stopped, he began to speak.

"I have orders to burn the *Philadelphia* in the harbor of Tripoli," he said. "I'll need men. I'm warning you there will be great danger. But all those who are willing to go, step forward."

There was a single movement toward Decatur. Every officer, seaman, and boy had stepped forward at the same time!

"But I can't take all of you," Decatur cried.

Grumblings of disappointment welled up. Some men began to push their way to the front. It hurt Decatur to have to choose among them. Yet he must.

"Mr. Herrmann," he called to the ship's doctor, "you examined the men last week. Bring the records to my cabin."

In a choked voice he praised the men and officers for their fine spirit, then hurried inside.

During the next hour, Decatur and the doctor selected sixty-two men with the best records for physical fitness.

"And I make sixty-three, sir," said the doctor, adding his name to the list he had made. "You'll need me to care for any who may be wounded."

It was useless to try to persuade him to stay with the *Enterprise*. He was determined to go. And so were Decatur's officers.

Decatur took them all. With his sixty-seven men and officers, he went quickly aboard the ketch which was now called the *Intrepid*. There they were joined by the midshipmen whom Commodore Preble had selected, and a

[*123*]

dark-haired Sicilian named Salvadore Catalano.

"The commodore sent me to be your pilot," Catalano told Decatur. "I know Tripoli harbor like the back of my hand. I can also speak the language of the people. And I do not like the Barbary pirates, for they raid our merchant vessels."

So it was that seventy-five men set sail early that evening in the *Intrepid*. The ketch was followed by the *Siren*. This was a brig commanded by Decatur's boyhood friend, Charles Stewart. Lieutenant Stewart had offered to accompany the *Intrepid* and to cover Decatur's retreat from Tripoli. And the commodore had accepted Stewart's offer.

As they sailed out of Syracuse, the sea was calm and the sky clear. Nevertheless, it was very uncomfortable for everyone on the ketch. There were not enough bunks for even a third of the men. Decatur, three officers, and the doctor were in the tiny cabin. Six midshipmen and the pilot, Catalano, shared a platform built over the water casks. They could not sit up without bumping their heads.

On the other side of the ship, there was another platform which eight men shared. The rest of the crew slept among the kegs and barrels of food, gunpowder, and fire-making material in the hold.

But there was not a single complaint from anyone. Not even when they were caught in a storm and for five days it seemed the towering waves would crush the little *Intrepid*. The crew were in the best of spirits as they went over with Decatur the exact details of how they would set fire to the *Philadelphia*. Each man became letter-perfect in what he had to do. As always, Decatur's own fearlessness and cheerful sharing of his men's hardships inspired them all.

Around nine o'clock at night, eight days later, the *Intrepid* arrived outside the harbor of Tripoli. Decatur sent all but twelve men down into the hold. Then he joined the pilot, Catalano, at the helm. The pilot steered for the mouth of the harbor. The *Siren* was left behind in the open sea to wait for them.

Under a light breeze, the ketch crept slowly through the water. If any person saw her stealing closer and closer to the *Philadelphia,* he was not alarmed. She looked exactly like any one of many small Barbary coast vessels.

There were lanterns aglow on the *Phila-delphia*. Some of the pirate crew, with tur-baned heads and scimitars glinting at their belts, could be seen walking about on deck.

The *Intrepid* was less than sixty feet away from the big ship when she was hailed.

"What ship is that?" demanded a watchman in Tripolitanese, leaning over the rail of the *Philadelphia*. "Who are you?"

For a moment those on the ketch scarcely breathed. Then at a nudge from Decatur, the pilot, Catalano, answered in the same language.

"We lost our anchors during the gale," he said. "Would you let us tie up to your ship until we can fetch some anchors from shore?"

"Very well. Very well," replied the watchman. "I'll send a boat with a line."

When the pirates rowed up in their boat, Catalano said, "Heave us the line."

The rope cut through the air, and one end fell on the deck of the ketch. The Americans grabbed it with eager hands and began to haul. No one spoke. The pirates must not hear the sound of foreign voices.

Little by little, the *Intrepid* was hauled closer to the *Philadelphia* as Decatur and his crew pulled and strained on the rope. From their rowboat, the pirates were watching the men in the ketch. Splashes of yellow light from the big ship's lanterns fell on the water around them. In a few minutes, the *Intrepid* slipped alongside the *Philadelphia* with no more noise than a shadow.

Then, of a sudden, a terrified cry came from

the pirates in the rowboat. *"Americanos!"* they screamed.

The cry was repeated on the ship. *"Americanos!"* It was echoed from deck to deck, *"Americanos! Americanos!"*

There were sounds of feet scurrying over the planks. Scimitars flashed in upflung hands. The Tripolitans, their wide breeches puffing out, ran here and there. They did not know where to look for the *Americanos*.

"Board!" Decatur cried to his men. And he sprang for the chains at the side of the ship. He reached the rail in a quick rush. Drawing his sword, he jumped to the deck. In an instant, two of his midshipmen were beside him.

The group of pirates in front of them fell back. Then through the gangway, the ports, and over the rail poured the Americans. Panic-stricken, the pirates swarmed forward toward the bow.

Decatur gathered his men around him. Then he gave the watchword. "Philadelphia!" he yelled.

With uplifted swords, the Americans rushed upon the pirate crew. The pirates turned and fled. They tumbled over the bow and fell over the sides. They jumped from the rail and through the gunports. They climbed down lines. Like dry leaves before the autumn wind they scattered to the various boats in the harbor.

In ten minutes the ship was cleared of pirates. The Americans were left in possession. Decatur gazed longingly over the warship. If only they could save her! But he knew they never would be able to tow her out of the harbor with the little ketch.

"Fire her!" Decatur cried. At once his men got from the ketch what they needed to set their fires. And they ran to their assigned places—the hold, storerooms, powder magazines, everywhere. Decatur had worked out the plan so carefully with his men in advance, that fires were set all over the ship at exactly the right moment.

As the Americans dashed up again to the fresh air, clouds of smoke trailed after them. Decatur sent his men back to the *Intrepid*. He stood on deck watching until the flashes of flame rose from every hatchway. Then, clutching a rope, he lowered himself into the ketch and called out, "Cut the lines and shove off!"

The men broke out the oars and pulled away from the ship. She was blazing from one end to the other. The pirates had been so taken by surprise and so confused that no guns had been fired up to this time. But now the Americans could no longer keep from cheering wildly over their success. Their voices rose in cheer after cheer that rang out across the harbor waters.

As though the cheering were a signal, enemy guns began to roar. With shot throwing up spray all around them, the Americans hoisted sail. And the ketch glided swiftly out into the harbor. At the entrance, boats of the

Siren met them. The men were overjoyed at
their safe return. They could scarcely believe
that no one in Decatur's crew had been hurt,
except one man. And he was
only slightly injured.

When the *Intrepid* came
up to the *Siren*, outside in the
open sea, Lieutenant Stewart
was standing at the rail. He
was waiting to congratulate
his old school-and-shipmate.

"I only wish I could have
been there with you, Ste-

phen," he said. "Then it would really have been just like old times."

"Never mind," Decatur consoled him. "There'll be more fighting. The Barbary pirates aren't whipped yet. The commodore," he smiled, "will have something in store for us by the time we get back to Syracuse."

CHAPTER TWELVE

The Battle with the Pirates

WHEN Decatur returned to Syracuse he suggested to Preble that it might be a good idea to make an attack on the pirates of Tripoli immediately. But the commodore shook his head.

"You have done excellent work in burning the *Philadelphia*," he said. "You've shown good judgment and handled your men well. But as for attacking Tripoli now—" Again he shook his head.

"Winter is no time for such an attack," he went on. "There are too many storms. If we were caught in one of the great gales off the African coast, we'd lose our whole squadron. No, I'm going to look around for some more boats. Then later we'll attack when we can depend on having good weather."

[*133*]

So the fleet remained at the naval base on the island of Sicily for several months. During this time Decatur worked hard, but he enjoyed himself, too. His brother James was also stationed at Syracuse and so were his old friends, Somers and Stewart.

One day in midsummer the four young men were walking together through a grove of wild fig trees. It was a beautiful morning. Never had the pomegranates seemed so rosy, or the cypress trees so silvery green.

"We've met so many nice people and had such good times here in Syracuse that I'll be sorry to leave," Somers said.

Decatur laughed. "I'll be glad to see some action again," he declared. "Did you know that the King of Sicily has loaned us six gunboats and two bomb vessels, all equipped with guns, ammunition, and crews?"

Stewart whistled in amazement. "That's good news!" he exclaimed. "Now let the pirates beware!"

James turned to his brother. "How soon are we going to sail, Stephen?" he asked.

"It won't be long now," Stephen replied with a smile. And it wasn't.

Only a few days later the whole American fleet of fifteen vessels set sail. And by the third of August they had all arrived off Tripoli.

Aboard the *Enterprise,* Decatur stood beside the helmsman to oversee the steering. At the same time he kept a sharp watch on the flagship *Constitution.* Preble's orders to the squadron were given by means of signal flags

hoisted high above the deck. Every commander of a vessel knew what to do by reading the signals.

Decatur saw the American flag go up on the *Constitution.* He ordered the Stars and Stripes run up on the *Enterprise.* All the other ships

[*135*]

broke out their American colors. The flags waved bravely in the noonday sun.

From his castle, the Bashaw, ruler of Tripoli, saw the squadron with colors flying, and knew the Americans were coming to fight. The Bashaw was not worried. He felt very safe behind his batteries of hundreds of guns. And his twenty-four gunboats, warships, and galleys in the harbor.

Decatur saw another flag raised on the *Constitution*. That was the signal he had been waiting for. It was the signal to attack.

"Wear ship!" Decatur ordered his men.

The *Enterprise* sailed to the left of the harbor. She was followed by the other vessels in Decatur's division. Decatur's friend, Somers, on the *Nautilus* led his division to the right of the harbor.

The two American bomb vessels forged ahead toward the city's gun batteries. They began shooting into the city. Of a sudden, guns from shore as well as from the ships in the harbor opened fire on the Americans.

Decatur headed his division directly for the group of nine gunboats coming toward him from the east side of the port. He saw Somers head for the five enemy gunboats on the west. At the same instant, he saw James swing his boat away from Somers' line. Swiftly, James brought his boat into line behind the *Enterprise*.

Decatur snatched up a leather speaking trumpet and started to call to his brother. Then he dropped the trumpet. There was no use confusing James by sending him back to his own division. Besides, the enemy gunboats were pouring a shower of cannon and musket balls into the American line. Decatur had to give all his attention to the attack.

He advanced, firing round after round into the enemy. James was right behind him. They drew close to the gunboats. Decatur blasted at one of the boats, wrecking the masts and the rigging. Water was flung high in the air as the gunboat heeled over.

"Grappling irons!" shouted Decatur.

Quickly, men ran with great hooks which they threw across the rail of the gunboat and dragged her up to the *Enterprise*.

"Pikes, pistols, swords, battle axes!" Decatur ordered. "Board!"

Waving his sword, Decatur leaped across to

[*137*]

the gunboat. His men, armed with pikes, pistols, axes, and swords, sprang after him. As Decatur landed on deck, he glanced to his left. He was just in time to catch a glimpse of James. His brother was balanced on the rail of another enemy gunboat, ready to jump aboard.

The next second Decatur and his men were engaged in a hand-to-hand battle with the pirates on the gunboat. The terrible struggle lasted ten minutes. In that time Decatur with his well-trained crew overcame the hard fighting Tripolitans.

Decatur had a tow line secured to the gunboat. He returned to the *Enterprise* and began hauling his prize away. He was passing James's ship when he heard:

"Your brother! Decatur, your brother's wounded! He's been captured! He's over there!" the men shouted. They pointed to the largest of the enemy gunboats. It was the same one Decatur had seen James trying to board earlier.

At once, Decatur ordered his lieutenant and part of his crew to board the gunboat he had captured. He set his prize adrift and headed back with the *Enterprise*. Fighting his way through the enemy's line, he ran his ship up to the big enemy gunboat. He jumped upon the deck. Immediately behind him were Reuben James, the quarter gunner, and ten others.

The Tripolitans rushed at them. They put up fierce resistance. It was some time before Decatur, hacking this way and that with his sword, could single out the captain. The Tripolitan was a big giant of a man, armed with a long iron pike. Decatur dashed at him with uplifted sword. The pirate lunged at Decatur with the pike. Decatur struck at it with his sword. The blade of the sword broke off at the hilt.

Again the pirate raised his pike and brought it down. Decatur parried the blow with his arm. The sharp point tore his arm and chest. But Decatur jerked away and, springing aside, grabbed the pike. He and the pirate grappled. In their struggle, they both fell to the deck, rolling over and over.

By this time the other Americans and Tripolitans were fighting in a violent free-for-all around Decatur and the pirate captain.

[*139*]

Suddenly, one of the Tripolitans, seeing Decatur down, struck at him with a scimitar. Reuben James darted in to save Decatur. The blow caught Reuben across the side of his head, cutting him badly.

Quickly, Decatur drew a loaded pistol from his belt. Cocking it, he fired at the Tripolitan, who staggered backward. The pirate captain rolled away, killed by the sword thrust of one of Decatur's men.

Getting to his feet, Decatur stood with his crew of Americans. They held off the pirates until more men could join them from the nearest American ships.

Decatur then took over the gunboat. This second prize was made fast to the *Enterprise*.

The battle was over. The Americans had in all captured three gunboats, sunk three more, and battered the city severely enough so that people were fleeing to the open country. The Americans had won the first victory over the Barbary pirates.

The signal flag, "Retire from action," flew above the *Constitution*. Under the protective screen of gunfire from the frigate, Decatur's division with its prizes and Somers' with his, streamed out of the harbor.

His duty to his country over, Decatur went in search of his brother. He found him below decks. James was so badly wounded that he lived only a few minutes. The day's victory was no longer bright and glorious for Stephen Decatur. His heart was filled with sadness as he sat beside his slain brother.

CHAPTER THIRTEEN

Southern Cruise

IT WAS April in Norfolk, Virginia. It was a day of blue sky and blue water. From where they stood on the pebbly beach, Decatur, his wife Susan, and brother John could see the frigate. The ship, anchored at the mouth of Chesapeake Bay, lay in the full light of the morning sun.

"That's the frigate *United States,*" Decatur told Susan. "I was a boy when I went into the New Jersey forest to get the logs to build that ship. It seems only yesterday."

"I remember when you went aboard the *United States* as a midshipman," John said. "I was just a little shaver then. I wasn't even in the Navy."

"And I can remember five years ago when

"That's the frigate United States,*"*
Decatur told Susan

I first met you," said Mrs. Decatur. She gave her husband's arm a fond squeeze. "You were Captain Stephen Decatur then. And you had been away for three years fighting the Barbary pirates and making yourself famous."

Decatur patted his wife's hand, thinking of all that had happened since his return to America five years earlier.

On his return he had been sent to the Naval station at Norfolk. There he had been placed in charge of a flotilla of gunboats. He had also fallen in love with beautiful Susan Wheeler, who was the daughter of a Norfolk merchant.

Now he and Susan had been married four years. John was a lieutenant in the Navy. And Stephen himself was a commodore.

"I wish my father had lived to know it," he thought, and he sighed.

"Come, Stephen," Mrs. Decatur urged, plucking at his sleeve. "We can't stay here all morning admiring your fine ship. You'll be sailing on her soon, and we have guests coming for a farewell luncheon."

The three of them made their way across the sandy beach to the road where a carriage belonging to Susan's father was waiting. Soon they reached the home of Susan's parents, where their friends were gathering.

The luncheon was a gay affair with much talking and laughter. Toward the end of the meal, a pretty young lady looked admiringly across the table at Stephen.

"And where are you going when you set sail?" she asked. "Or is it a secret?"

Decatur smiled. "It's no secret," he told her. "We shall be cruising up and down the coast trying to keep the British from bothering our American merchant ships. They've been at it too long and it's time they were stopped."

"I understand they've taken hundreds of men from American ships and forced them to serve in the British Navy," an elderly gentleman remarked.

"They've taken thousands, sir," Decatur said. "Some of them were men who had already deserted from the British Navy because they were poorly paid and badly fed. But most of them were good American citizens.

"The British need men to help them in the war they are waging with France. And they also want to prevent us from trading with foreign nations. But they'll not be able to take men from American ships much longer. Our Navy is growing stronger every day."

He cocked his head to one side as the tall clock near the stairs began to strike. "I'm afraid I must leave," he said, pushing his chair back from the table.

He said good-by to his wife and John and his friends. Soon he had set out in his gig across the harbor to his ship. When he reached the *United States,* the men lined up in a double row to receive him. The boatswain blew on his silver whistle to pipe him over the side. And the broad pennant of a commodore was hoisted as a signal that Commodore Decatur was on board ship.

To see his pennant flying up there gave him a special thrill. Here it was 1810 and he was a commodore, back on the same ship he had helped to build sixteen years before!

Protecting the coast was not too difficult a task. But Decatur wanted his men to be ready if they ever had to fight. So during the long spring days, he trained them in seamanship. And he had them practice at target shooting until they were fast and accurate.

After the daily drills and practice, however,

Decatur had time to study. He studied a subject that had interested him for a long time—natural history.

Very little was known about the offshore waters. There were no good charts to tell navigators where dangerous rocks and sandbars lay hidden. Or how deep or shallow the sea was in places. Day after day, Decatur had men swinging the long lead line, taking soundings. He would stand by, setting down the depth of the water. And he would mark spots on a map to show where rocky ledges, sandy shoals, and islands lay.

He was curious too about the plants and creatures that lived in the ocean. For many years, he had been collecting and studying them. Now he invented a deep-water apparatus which he could use to bring up things from the unexplored bottom of the sea.

When the apparatus was finished, he was off the coast of South Carolina. Decatur ordered the ship hove to.

"We'll anchor here for a while," he told Reuben James, who was helping him get the device rigged up to a pulley. "The warm waters around here are full of marine life."

From the deck, he, Reuben, and some of the ship's company looked down upon the jellyfish, bobbing like pale cabbage heads on top of the water. Below in the green depths, they could see silver-sided fish and a glistening black eel, weaving in and out of the shadows cast by the ship's hull and masts.

"Ready?" asked Decatur, turning to Reuben James.

"Yes, sir," replied the other.

"Then lower away," Decatur said.

The apparatus looked like a huge clamshell. There was a hinge at the back, so the halves of the shell opened and shut in the manner of jaws. There was a rope for lowering and raising.

As Reuben James let out the rope, the apparatus fell with a splash into the water. It sank rapidly more than a hundred feet down to the soft ooze of the ocean floor.

A few minutes later, he hauled it up again. Decatur eased it over the rail and spilled its contents out into the big wooden tub which had been placed on deck.

As excited as though he were gazing at a pirate's treasure, Decatur sat on his heels be-

fore the tub with some of his officers and crew
gathered around him. For several minutes he
pored over the mud and brown slime. He
studied the tiny marine plants, pieces of bone
and fins, and three small
wriggling creatures.

"I've never seen any-
thing like them before.
Have you, sir?" asked Reuben James.

Decatur shook his head.
"No, I haven't. They're
some kind of shellfish.
Some kind of shrimp, in
fact."

"That's a queer snap-
ping sound they make," observed one of the officers.

*The United States Congress declared war
on England*

Decatur picked up one of the shrimp between thumb and finger to examine it. It was quite round in shape and less than an inch across. The shrimp had only one large claw. But it kept that one clicking like a pair of scissors.

Decatur glanced around with his quick, eager smile. He was pleased over his discovery. "It wasn't bad for a first haul with a new contraption," he remarked, getting up. "I've three new specimens of shellfish. Fetch me a bucket of sea water for them, Reuben. Then we'll try making another haul."

In the following months, Decatur continued his research into the strange life beneath the water. He brought up a great variety of sea life from depths which had never been explored before. And he made a number of discoveries of unknown plants and fish.

Meanwhile the trouble between the Americans and the British had been growing worse. On June 18, 1812, the United States Congress declared war on England. And Stephen Decatur had no more time for study and research.

CHAPTER FOURTEEN

"Clear Ship for Action!"

IT WAS the night of June 19. The air was warm in Norfolk, and the servants had opened the windows of the Wheelers' drawing room. Through the windows drifted the sound of men's rough voices.

"Free trade and sailors' rights! That's what we're fighting for! We licked 'em before. We'll lick 'em again. Free trade and sailors' rights!" the men were shouting.

The little company of Susan and Stephen Decatur's friends, who were seated in the room before Susan's harp, turned their heads to listen. Underneath the chanting, they could hear feet, tramping like muffled drums on the dusty road outside. The Norfolk militia was marching down to guard the water front. The sounds rose and died away in the distance as swiftly as a gust of wind passing by.

The guests turned back to the music. Mrs. Decatur plucked the strings of her harp and sang:

> *"Hark! now the drums beat up again,*
> *For all true soldiers, gentlemen,*
> *Then let us join and march today*
> *Over the hills and far away."*

After the song was over, there was a small thunder of applause. Mrs. Decatur rose, smiling and bowing.

"Don't stop, Susan. Give us one more song before we go," pleaded Decatur's old friend, Captain Charles Stewart. "That last was a rousing good song for the soldiers. Now sing one for us sailors who are leaving tonight."

"Just one more," begged the others.

"Very well," Mrs. Decatur agreed, sitting down again. "I'll sing 'Heart of Oak' for the three sailors—John, Charles, and Stephen.

> *"Heart of oak are our ships,*
> *Heart of oak are our men;*
> *We always are ready, steady, boys, steady,*
> *We'll fight and we'll conquer again and again."*

[*153*]

Decatur watched her with love and admiration. It was good to have this quiet evening at home. And to have old friends around him. He felt that perhaps it gave them all a feeling of united strength for the struggle ahead on land and sea.

This war with England was going to be a desperate one. For the American Army was small. Most of the fighting on land would have to be done by companies of militia made up of volunteers. As for the U. S. Navy—what were twenty warships and some useless gunboats against the English Navy of nearly a thousand sail!

There was a loud bang of the knocker on the front door. It came just as the song was ended. It resounded in the moment's silence like the crack of the clapper in a great iron bell. The women looked startled. The men jumped up.

Then Decatur laughed. Drawing his watch from his pocket, he observed, "That's only the mate come to fetch us in the cart. It's eight o'clock. Time to get back to our ships."

Followed by the company, Decatur, Stewart, and John went into the hall. They took their swords from the table and buckled them on.

"Good-by, my dear. I shall write you when my ship reaches New York," Decatur told Susan and kissed her fondly.

Mrs. Decatur stood on the porch steps and watched them drive off. They appeared for an instant in the light of the lamp on a post beside the road. Their three arms went up at the same time. Her last glimpse of them was three hats being waved vigorously above the bouncing, two-wheeled cart.

A few days later, Decatur was in New York harbor with the frigate *United States*. There he joined the squadron of Commodore John Rodgers. By five o'clock on the afternoon of the same day, the squadron had put to sea. Decatur had only time enough before leaving to write a note to Susan, and send it by a harbor boatman to give to the first postboy riding south.

For seventy-two days the squadron cruised together in search of enemy ships. They captured seven and took them into the harbor of Boston. Then each ship in the squadron was ordered to set out alone. Decatur set the course of the *United States* across the Atlantic, toward Portugal and Spain.

It was October. The ship bowled along in the sunshine through the green waters near the coast. Overhead, flocks of shore birds were migrating, following the age-old flyways from the Arctic to the warm lands of the South. The shrill "quee-ah!" of plovers and sharp "tee-arrr!" of the terns could be heard clearly among the booming and twittering voices of the other birds.

Then as the ship sailed farther from land, the color of the waters changed from green to deep blue. And only the flutelike notes of the phalaropes were heard in the sky as the little brown birds went wheeling and dipping, on their way south with the sun.

Decatur always left orders with the officer

who was in charge of the deck from four to eight o'clock in the morning, to wake him before dawn. The best time to forecast the weather, he said, was at daybreak. Sunday, October 25, the officer knocked on Decatur's cabin door.

"Eight bells, sir," he called. Four o'clock in the morning.

"Very good," Decatur answered. "I'll be on deck shortly." Getting up, he dressed in his homespun uniform, for the weather was warm. And he put on his straw hat with the brim, for the sun would be hot later on.

Stepping out on the quarter-deck, he stopped to speak to the helmsman to get the position of the ship.

"Latitude twenty-nine degrees north. Longitude twenty-nine degrees west, sir," replied the man.

"Not far from the island of Madeira then," Decatur observed. "British merchant ships take this sea lane past Madeira and the coasts of Portugal and Spain. Let's hope we meet one of the fleets."

"Aye, sir. We'll manage to cut out a rich prize or two from the convoy, if we do." The officer gave a wry chuckle. "Can't wait to get my hands on them lobsterbacks."

Decatur walked to starboard and looked over the side. The waters were aflame with lights that flashed and faded. In the autumn, the sea was glowing with phosphorescence.

[158]

The waves rolling against the sides of the ship flickered with the blues and greens and reds of a driftwood fire.

Decatur loved the sight of the October sea. He gazed down for a long time at the path of stars his ship made, cutting through the water. Presently, he sniffed a cool, fresh breeze. Gulls, coming from the near-by land, circled above the mast-tops, screaming noisily. And after a while the sun rose, hot and copper bright.

Decatur glanced upward at the sky. There was a small cloud directly overhead. As the sun crept higher, the cloud gradually vanished.

"We're going to have another good day," Decatur remarked to the man at the wheel. "As the people of the East say, 'the sun ate up the storm cloud.'"

The cook was up and about. Decatur could hear the clang of iron kettles in the galley. He saw Jack Creamer, who was ten years old and the youngest aboard, come on deck with the ship's cat under one arm. Jack had a plate of food in his left hand. Putting the tin plate down, he set the cat in front of it. Then he scampered back to the galley at the cook's howled "Come here, younker, and tend to your business!"

The routine of the day had begun. After looking round upon the sea, empty of sails as usual, Decatur went back to his cabin. He had his breakfast. Shortly before eight o'clock, he returned to the quarter-deck. Lieutenant Allen was waiting to go over the orders for the day. They were standing talking together when they heard the lookout at the foremast call, "Deck there! Sail ho!"

"Where away?" Decatur asked quickly.

"Off the starboard bow," replied the lookout.

"Can you make her out?" Decatur asked.

"She's a square-rigged vessel. Has a coachwhip pennant flying at the masthead," the lookout shouted excitedly.

"A warship, sir! She's a man-of-war!" Allen exclaimed. The narrow pennant, called a coachwhip, at the top of a mast was a special flag which all nations used on their vessels of war.

Again the lookout called down. "She's a big frigate. She's bearing down on us, sir. They're hoisting their colors." He was silent for a moment, then he cried, "She's English!"

At once, Decatur gave the command: "All hands clear the ship for action!"

To the sound of fife and drum, the men scattered to their various firing stations. The boatswain got his men ready to repair any damage to the rigging. The carpenter and his crew fetched their mauls and a supply of wooden plugs to jam in the holes made by gunshot. Men all over the ship went into action.

[*161*]

Decatur caught sight of little Jack Creamer as he darted into the galley, carrying the ship's cat to safety. In an instant, the boy was back again and running aft toward the quarter-deck. Coming up to Decatur, he touched his hat in salute.

"Commodore," he said breathlessly, "will you please have my name put down on the muster roll?"

"Why, lad?" Decatur asked curiously.

"Because, sir, I'm sure we're going to win. And I want to know for certain my name's down so I can get my share of the prize money."

Decatur nodded gravely and, turning to Lieutenant Allen, said, "Enter Jack Creamer's name on the muster roll. Put him down for one share, the same as any able seaman."

"Thank you, sir," Jack said happily. He dashed back down the deck to the gun crew of which he was the powder monkey. "Now, when they take that big frigate into port," he thought, "I'll get extra pay for helping to take a prize, the same as the other men."

It never occurred to Jack that the Americans might not win. He believed, as did all the ship's officers and men, that Commodore Decatur knew how to lick any vessel afloat. All Jack Creamer had to do was keep the powder handy for the gun crew the way he had been taught.

There was silence aboard ship once all were at their stations. Decatur watched the British frigate draw nearer.

"That's the *Macedonian*," he said to Allen. "I know her captain—Captain Carden. A number of years ago, he and I used to visit back and forth. He's a fine man and a brave officer. Now we meet again—this time in battle."

The distance between the two ships narrowed. Decatur told the sailing master to get the range for the guns. Then he commanded the gun captains, "Level your guns! Run them out! Fire!"

It was shooting at long range. But Decatur had so carefully drilled his gunners that within less than half an hour's firing, one of the masts of the *Macedonian* had been shot away. Immediately, the enemy bore up for action at closer range. For the British were not skilled at gunnery.

As the *Macedonian* sailed nearer, the firing of the *United States* became so rapid that the ship seemed to be a mass of flames and smoke from one end to the other. Another one of the *Macedonian's* masts toppled over.

"Look, sailor!" cried a gun captain to one of his men near Decatur, "we've made a brig out of that frigate already. She's only got two masts left."

"Take good aim, my lad, at the mainmast," Decatur told him, "and she will soon be a sloop. She'll be left with only one mast." Turning to another gun captain, he said,

"Aim at the yellow streak around her hull. Her spars and rigging are going fast enough. But we'll have to put a few more holes in her hull."

Very soon, the *Macedonian's* two remaining masts were so badly damaged that they were useless. The British frigate was being battered to splinters. On board there were so many killed and wounded, there were few left to man the guns. There were only eleven wounded on the *United States*.

Within seventeen minutes after the vessels began their battle in close action, the *Macedonian* was a complete wreck. She struck her colors.

A boat brought the captain of the *Macedonian* over to the *United States.* Decatur met him on the quarter-deck. The Englishman appeared dazed.

"Captain Carden," Decatur said, bowing.

"I am an undone man," Carden said in a choked voice. He offered his sword to Decatur.

Decatur waved the sword away. "Sir," he

said, "I cannot receive the sword of a man who has so bravely defended his ship."

Decatur gave Lieutenant Allen orders to take command of the *Macedonian*. He had Captain Carden shown to a comfortable cabin. Then, going to his own cabin, Decatur sent for Jack Creamer.

When the boy came hurrying in, the commodore greeted him heartily. "Well, Jack," he said, "we have taken His Majesty's warship. And your share of the prize, if we get her safely in, may be about two hundred dollars. What will you do with it?"

"I will send half of it to my mother, sir," Jack answered promptly. "And the other half shall pay for my schooling."

"Now that is very wise," Decatur assured him. "One of these days, let's have a talk about your becoming a midshipman. I think you have the makings of a proper seaman."

"I've always wanted to be in the Navy, sir," Jack said. "If I'm a midshipman, will I be on your ship?"

Decatur nodded. "You will be. Even if I have to write a special letter about it to the Secretary of the Navy," he promised.

[*167*]

CHAPTER FIFTEEN

Farewell to the Sea

AFTER two years the war with Great Britain came to an end. Now Decatur and other American Navy men could turn their attention to North Africa where the Barbary States were up to their old tricks. As soon as the United States or any other nation turned its back, the Barbary corsairs returned to their piracy. While England and the United States were fighting each other, the pirates had been busy again, robbing ships and selling crews and passengers for slaves.

Decatur was sent with a squadron to the Mediterranean Sea. He was to fight if necessary to make the pirates quit molesting American ships.

By June, 1815, he had reached Algiers on his ship *Guerrière*. He captured the flagship of the Algerine squadron in a battle. Decatur so impressed the ruler of Algiers with the power of the U. S. Navy that the Dey agreed to sign a peace treaty. He also returned all property which had been stolen from American ships and some Americans who had been taken as slaves.

Tunis was next. Into that port, Decatur sailed on July 26. He anchored the *Guerrière* and the other ships of his squadron within firing distance of the city. He sent his lieutenant ashore with a message for the American consul, Mr. M. M. Noah.

"Please go see the Bey of Tunis," Decatur instructed Mr. Noah. "Tell him that he has twelve hours in which to pay for the two captured American ships. Their value is forty-six thousand dollars. If he fails to pay for the damage done the United States, my squadron will begin firing on Tunis."

When the lieutenant had left with the message, Decatur called Jack Creamer.

"Get two men and a lead line, Jack," he told the boy. "Lower one of the boats. We're going to take some soundings."

"Yes, sir!" Jack said with a wide grin and

[*169*]

quick toss of his head. "Going to take the squadron right up to the city walls, I expect, sir!"

Decatur gave him an answering grin. "I may have to."

An hour later, the ruler of Tunis was standing with Mr. Noah, the American consul, in front of a window in his castle. The Bey was looking through a telescope at a small boat. Two American sailors were rowing

while a third sailor and a boy were swinging
the lead line to measure the
depth of the water.

The Bey handed the tele-
scope to Mr. Noah. "Those
Americans out there are taking soundings of the harbor.
What does that mean?" he demanded.

Mr. Noah looked at the boat. He smiled wryly as he recognized Decatur, dressed in sailor's middy and bell-bottomed trousers. The commodore was never afraid of losing the respect of his men by doing any sort of sailor's work himself, thought Noah.

"It means that Commodore Stephen Decatur wants to make sure how close to shore he can get with our warships," Noah answered calmly. "The commodore meant what he said about attacking Tunis, Your Highness."

"You said Stephen Decatur!" exclaimed the Bey. "I know this admiral. He is the same man who burned the frigate *Philadelphia,* in the war with Tripoli; isn't he?"

"Yes, the same," Noah said.

"Hum!" grunted the Bey. He peered suspiciously at Noah. "Why do you Americans not speak the truth?" he asked. "You went to war with England, a nation with a great fleet. And you said you took their frigates in equal fight. How can this be true?"

"Well, sir," replied Noah, "it is. Take another look out there." He handed the telescope back to the Bey. "Do you see that tall ship in the bay? The one with the blue flag?

[*172*]

That is the *Guerrière,* taken from the British."

The Bey squinted an eye and peered at the harbor. "Yes, I see," he said.

Noah went on. "See that ship near the small island, the *Macedonian?* She was captured by Decatur in an equal fight. That sloop over there—the *Peacock*—was taken in battle."

The Bey laid down the telescope. Picking up a tortoise-shell comb from a low table, he walked over to a divan and sat down cross-legged. For several minutes he combed his beard and gazed fixedly at the American flags waving over the waters of the bay.

At last he said, "You Americans do speak truth, I see. Tell your admiral that everything shall be settled to his liking."

It was. Decatur, with a treaty of peace in his strongbox, was on his way to Tripoli within a few days.

There, the Bashaw had every reason to say, "I know this admiral." For the ruler of Tripoli would never forget the burning of the *Philadelphia* outside his own city walls.

The Bashaw paid $25,000 damages to the United States and released the ten people he held as slaves. He even fired a thirty-one gun salute from his great stone castle in honor of the Americans.

In just seventy-one days, Decatur had accomplished what he had set out to do. He had obtained treaties of peace from all of the Barbary States. Before the middle of November, he had returned to New York with his squadron.

The newspapers announced his arrival in bold, black headlines. Dinners were held in his honor. He received letters from all over the nation, congratulating him on his success. One of the letters was official and very important. It came from the Secretary of the U. S. Navy.

Decatur tore it open and read: "You are hereby appointed to the board of Navy Commissioners."

A Navy Commissioner! His country could not give him any higher post. Decatur felt humble and grateful. But it meant that he must give up his life at sea. It meant working in an office—not on the deck of a ship, open to the sun and wind. It meant setting up rules and regulations for the Navy. Planning harbor defenses and navy yards. Deciding upon the kinds of ships to be built. Constantly working with pen and ink and paper.

On his journey south to Norfolk, Virginia, Decatur thought, "There is all the difference in the world in being a commodore in the Navy and living at sea, and being a Commissioner of the Navy and living on land."

It was going to be difficult to change his whole way of life. Yet there was one great happiness to look forward to. He and Susan would be together.

They would buy a home in Washington. In his travels he had bought beautiful pieces with which to furnish it. He and Susan could enjoy the companionship of their many friends in their home. He would have time to study. Susan had her music in which they both took a deep interest. Decatur began to whistle cheerfully under his breath as he thought about all these comforting things. He could leave the life aboard ship to young fellows like Midshipman Jack Creamer. That lad was going to make a good Navy man, Decatur concluded with satisfaction.

When he reached Norfolk, he found that

Susan's friends and his had planned a big celebration. It took place in a hotel, for there was not enough room in any house to hold all the people who wanted to honor Stephen Decatur.

The hotel dining room was draped with flags. Among them were the battle-torn pennants of ships that Decatur had captured from the British, the French and the Barbary corsairs. At the long table were seated navy and army officers, public officials, merchants, plantation owners, and many old friends.

Susan and the other ladies were scarcely brighter in their gay gowns than the officers in their colored uniforms or the townsmen with their vests of silk brocade.

Everyone was in a joyful mood. They laughed and joked over a fine dinner of fish, roast beef, stuffed squab and spring vegetables, cake, cheese and fruits. There were speeches acclaiming the Navy and praising Decatur's part in the victory over the pirates. Then each man in turn stood up to pay a tribute of praise to his country.

"The Mediterranean!" exclaimed a rich planter. "The sea of Greek, Roman, and of American glory!"

"Our national glory!" said a merchant. "It is worth all the dangers, hardships, and sacrifices we have undergone."

"Our national honor!" one of the captains said. "It is the nation's brightest jewel!"

Round the table rang the words, hailing the glory of the United States. Finally Decatur's turn came. He rose, tall and erect, yet easy and graceful. His black eyes flashed.

"Our country!" he cried in a stirring voice. "In her relations with foreign nations, may she always be in the right. But our country, right or wrong!"

A burst of cheering followed his words. Then everybody rose from the table. It was time to go home.

Home to the Decaturs was now Washington. They lived in a small house near the Navy Building where Decatur worked, helping to build the U. S. Navy into a great military service. Since he was ashore to stay, he decided that he and Susan should have a beautiful home. So a fine brick mansion was built for them on President's Square in Washington.

Many friends came to see them there. And the mansion was the scene of gay parties for important people from all over the world.

The great house was well known, too, to the poor people of the city. For that was where the commodore lived who sent food to needy families. It belonged to Commissioner Decatur, who gave other needy families their winter's wood. Paid the rent for a widow and her children. Found a job for an old sailor. Helped and encouraged boys like Jack Creamer to get an education.

Life was full and pleasant for the Decaturs. The days and weeks slipped by quickly.

Decatur was forty years old. And the day was June 12, 1819, when a letter from a former U. S. Navy officer changed everything for him. This was the letter:

> Hampton, Virginia
>
> SIR,
>
> I have been informed in Norfolk that you have said that you could safely insult me, or words to that effect. If you have said so, you will, no doubt admit it. I shall expect to hear from you.
>
> JAMES BARRON.

Decatur studied the letter thoughtfully. What did it mean? James Barron had been captain of the *Essex* and of the *New York* at the time when Decatur had served on those ships as first lieutenant. The two men had never been good friends, though they had always managed to get along together. Now it looked as if Barron were trying to stir up a real quarrel. Why?

"It must be because I advised the Secretary of the Navy not to make him the commander of that new ship *Columbus*," Decatur thought. "I don't think he's fit to command a ship. But if he feels I've insulted him, I'll write and tell him it isn't so."

Sitting down at his desk, Decatur wrote to Barron as he had planned. Back came another angry letter from Barron. Decatur wrote again. So did Barron. Letters flowed between the two men. And each letter grew more bitter and deadly. At last Barron wrote that only a duel between them would settle the affair. He asked Decatur to name the time and place.

In the past, many quarrels between Navy men had been settled by duelling. Decatur did not think the custom was a good one. But he felt that he must uphold his own honor and the honor of the Navy. Reluctantly he accepted Barron's challenge.

[*179*]

On the morning of March 22, 1820, Decatur got up early. He had told Mrs. Decatur nothing of what was to happen that day. After bidding her a cheerful good-by, he walked down Pennsylvania Avenue to Beale's Hotel on Capitol Hill in Washington. There he had breakfast with two of his friends, Commodore William Bainbridge and Samuel Hambleton of the Navy.

Breakfast over, they set out in a carriage for Bladensburg, a few miles away. In a field near the village, they met James Barron and his friend, Captain Elliott. Decatur and Barron took their stands, ten paces apart. Bainbridge loaded Decatur's pistol. Elliott loaded Barron's. Decatur and Barron were given their pistols.

Bainbridge then spoke the words quickly and sharply, "Present arms! One, two, three!"

At the word "two," both Decatur and Barron fired. Barron fell, wounded in the right hip. Decatur stood upright for a moment. Then he fell, clutching his right side.

"I'm mortally wounded," he said quietly to Bainbridge, who had rushed over to him. Then he added with a moan, "I wish I had

[*180*]

fallen instead in defense of my country."

At ten o'clock that night, surrounded by his wife and relatives and friends, and with hundreds of people anxiously waiting outside the house, Decatur died.

The sad tidings were announced to the nation next morning. "A hero has fallen," the newspaper stories began. "Commodore Stephen Decatur, one of the first officers of the Navy, the pride of his country, the gallant and noble-hearted gentleman, is no more."

About the Author

DOWN ON THE GULF COAST of Southwest Texas where Iris Vinton lived as a child, the ranches stretched all along the water. So the cowboys knew almost as much about the sea and ships as they did about horses and cattle. They used to sit around the campfire, telling wonderful tales about storms, wrecks, buccaneers, and sea fights. Iris Vinton listened to them and remembered them, as she and other children climbed about old ships wrecked on the beach. It is no wonder that she soon began to write about ships and sailors. Besides writing stories for boys and girls, she edits the publications of the Boys' Clubs of America.

About the Artist

GRAHAM KAYE is a graduate of Cooper Union, in New York City. There he won a scholarship to the Art Students League and then went on to the Chicago Art Institute. His illustrations have appeared since in nearly all the leading magazines. He spent five years on a Government survey of glacial formation in Alaska and served a year during the war with the Army Engineers. He has toured every state in the Union exhibiting the right method of swimming the crawl. Swimming is still his hobby, and there is plenty of opportunity for that near where he lives, in St. Augustine, Florida.

"Names That Made History"

ENID LAMONTE MEADOWCROFT, *Supervising Editor*

THE STORY OF JOHN J. AUDUBON
By Joan Howard.   *Illustrated by Federico Castellon*

THE STORY OF CLARA BARTON
By Olive Price.   *Illustrated by Ruth Ives*

THE STORY OF GOOD QUEEN BESS
By Alida Sims Malkus.   *Illustrated by Douglas Gorsline*

THE STORY OF BUFFALO BILL
By Edmund Collier.   *Illustrated by Nicholas Eggenhofer*

THE STORY OF DANIEL BOONE
By William O. Steele.   *Illustrated by Warren Baumgartner*

THE STORY OF KIT CARSON
By Edmund Collier.   *Illustrated by Nicholas Eggenhofer*

THE STORY OF GEORGE WASHINGTON CARVER
By Arna Bontemps.   *Illustrated by Harper Johnson*

THE STORY OF CHRISTOPHER COLUMBUS
By Nina Brown Baker.   *Illustrated by David Hendrickson*

THE STORY OF CRAZY HORSE
By Enid LaMonte Meadowcroft.   *Illustrated by William Reusswig*

THE STORY OF DAVY CROCKETT
By Enid LaMonte Meadowcroft.   *Illustrated by C. B. Falls*

THE STORY OF GENERAL CUSTER
By Margaret Leighton.   *Illustrated by Nicholas Eggenhofer*

THE STORY OF STEPHEN DECATUR
By Iris Vinton.   *Illustrated by Graham Kaye*

THE STORY OF THOMAS ALVA EDISON
By Enid LaMonte Meadowcroft.   *Illustrated by Harve Stein*

THE STORY OF LEIF ERICSON
By William O. Steele.   *Illustrated by Pranas Lapé*

THE STORY OF STEPHEN FOSTER
By Esther M. Douty.   *Illustrated by Jo Polseno*

THE STORY OF BENJAMIN FRANKLIN
By Enid LaMonte Meadowcroft.   *Illustrated by Edward A. Wilson*